LE NOZZE DI FIGARO

(THE MARRIAGE OF FIGARO)

An Opera in Four Acts

Libretto by

LORENZO DA PONTE

Music by

W. A. MOZART

VOCAL SCORE
Including the Secco Recitatives

English Version by
RUTH AND THOMAS MARTIN

With an Essay on the
Story of the Opera by
NATHAN BRODER

Ed. 2021

G. SCHIRMER
New York

NOTE

G. SCHIRMER
New York

DRAMATIS PERSONAE

COUNT ALMAVIVA .... Baritone

COUNTESS ALMAVIVA .... Soprano

SUSANNA, her chambermaid .... Soprano
affianced to

FIGARO, valet to the Count .... Bass

CHERUBINO, the Count's page .... Soprano

MARCELLINA .... Mezzo Soprano

BASILIO, music master .... Tenor

DON CURZIO, a judge .... Tenor

BARTOLO, a doctor from Seville .... Bass

ANTONIO, the Count's gardener .... Bass
and Susanna's uncle

BARBARINA, his daughter .... Soprano

Country men and women, Court attendants, Hunters, and Servants

The scene is the castle of Count Almaviva, about three leagues from Seville

THE MARRIAGE OF FIGARO

One evening in the spring of 1783 Mozart visited his admirer and former landlord, Baron Raimund Wetzlar von Plankenstein, at the baron's home in Vienna. There he met an Italian writer, concerning whom he wrote to his father:

> Our poet here is now a certain Abbate da Ponte. He has an enormous amount to do in revising pieces for the theater and he has to write *per obbligo* an entirely new libretto for Salieri, which will take him two months. He has promised after that to write a new libretto for me. But who knows whether he will be able to keep his word—or will want to? For, as you are aware, these Italian gentlemen are very civil to your face. Enough, we know them! If he is in league with Salieri, I shall never get anything out of him. But indeed I should dearly love to show what I can do in an Italian opera![1]

Since this meeting was to result in one of the most important collaborations in the history of opera, and in the creation of three masterpieces—*Le Nozze di Figaro, Don Giovanni,* and *Così fan tutte*—, it may be well to sketch here the career of the less well known partner.

His real name was Emanuele Conegliano and he was born March 10, 1749, at Ceneda, a small town in northeastern Italy. His father, a Jew, was left a widower, and when Emanuele was fourteen had himself and his three sons baptized so that he could marry a young Catholic girl. In accordance with a custom of the time, the eldest son took the name of the sponsor, Monsignor Lorenzo da Ponte, bishop of Ceneda. Young Lorenzo studied in the seminary of the town and later at Portogruaro. By the time he was twenty-two he was giving instruction in rhetoric and the Italian language and had taken minor orders for the priesthood. From Portogruaro he went to Venice, where he eked out a precarious living by teaching and writing poetry and by less legitimate activities, plunging zestfully into the dissolute life of the Venetian Republic. He got into, and out of, one scrape after another until, in 1779, the patience of even the lenient authorities of Venice was overtaxed, and they banished da Ponte from all Venetian territories. He made his way to Vienna, armed with a letter of introduction to Antonio Salieri, court composer to Joseph II. There Salieri helped to get him appointed theater poet and da Ponte enjoyed some years of success, writing many librettos (including the three for Mozart) as well as poems for special occasions. After the death of Joseph II (1790) da Ponte left Vienna. Most of the next thirteen years (1792-1805) were spent in London, where he was for part of the time poet of the King's Theatre. In 1805 da Ponte, as a result of one of his frequent financial crises, came to the United States. He tried the grocery business, first in New York and then in Elizabethtown, N. J., returned to New York to teach Italian, attempted for eight years to establish himself as a business man in Sunbury, Pa., and for a year in Philadelphia, but came back in 1819 to New York. Here he taught Italian again and in 1825 was appointed professor of Italian Literature at Columbia College (a post that gave him

[1] Emily Anderson, *Letters of Mozart and His Family,* London, 1938, III, 1263 f. It was to Vienna that Mozart wanted to display his ability in the field of Italian opera. His last previous work of this sort. *Idomeneo* (1780-81), was written for Munich.

prestige but no salary). In the same year Manuel Garcia and his daughter Maria Malibran came to New York and da Ponte persuaded them to produce *Don Giovanni* (for the first time in America) at the Park Theater. In the 1820s da Ponte wrote his memoirs, which still make lively reading today, even though the author understandably glossed over or omitted the less savory episodes in his life, and his memory of events that took place thirty or forty years before he wrote about them is not reliable. He died in New York on August 17, 1838, at the age of eighty-nine.

* *
*

It was not two months but more than two years after Mozart reported his conversation with da Ponte to his father before the opportunity arose for them to work together. In 1785 Mozart was at the height of his creative powers and in greater demand as a composer than at any time before or after in his brief life. In that one year were published two symphonies (K.385 and 319), the six quartets dedicated to Haydn, three piano concertos (K.413-415), and the Fantasy and Sonata in C minor for piano (K.475 and 457), among other things. Leopold Mozart reported in a letter to his daughter dated November 3-4 that a journalist in Salzburg had remarked to him: "It is really astonishing to see what a number of compositions your son is publishing. In all the announcements of musical works I see nothing but Mozart. The Berlin announcements, when quoting the quartets, only add the following words: 'It is quite unnecessary to recommend these quartets to the public. Suffice it to say that they are the work of Herr Mozart.'"[2] But beneath all this activity was Mozart's burning desire to "show what I can do in an Italian opera"—a desire that had gnawed at him ever since he had come to Vienna in 1781 and that had led him to seek a suitable libretto even before he had met da Ponte. The latter finally kept his promise. Here is his own account. The time is the late summer or early fall of 1785.

> ... I began quietly thinking about the plays I was to write for my two dear friends Mozart and Martín [Vicente Martín y Soler]. As to the former, I readily perceived that the greatness of his genius demanded a subject which should be ample, elevated, and abounding in character and incident. When we were talking about it one day, he asked me if I could easily adapt Beaumarchais' comedy, *The Marriage of Figaro*. The proposal pleased me very well, and I promised to do as he wished. But there was a great difficulty to be overcome. Only a few days before, the Emperor had forbidden the company at the German theater to act this same comedy, as it was, he said, too outspoken for a polite audience. How could one now suggest it to him for an opera? Baron Wetzlar very generously offered to give me a very fair sum for the words and to have the opera produced in London or in France if it could not be done at Vienna. But I declined his offers and proposed that words and music should be written secretly and that we should await a favorable opportunity to show it to the theatrical managers or to the Emperor, which I boldly undertook to do. Martín was the only one to whom I told our great secret, and out of his regard for Mozart he very readily agreed to my postponing writing for him until I had finished *Figaro*.
>
> So I set to work, and as I wrote the words he composed the music for them. In six weeks all was ready. As Mozart's good luck would have it, they were in need of a new work at the theater. So I seized the opportunity and without saying anything to anybody, I went to the Emperor himself and offered him *Figaro*.

[2] Anderson, III, 1331.

"What!" he said, "Don't you know that Mozart, though excellent at instrumental music, has only written one opera, and that nothing very great?"

"Without Your Majesty's favor," I answered humbly, "I too should have written only one play in Vienna."

"That is true," he replied, "but I've forbidden this *Marriage of Figaro* to the German company."

"Yes," I said, "but as I was writing a play to be set to music and not a comedy, I have had to leave out a good many scenes and shorten a great many more, and I've left out and shortened whatever might offend the refinement and decorum of an entertainment at which Your Majesty presides. And as for the music, as far as I can judge it is extraordinarily fine."

"Very well," he answered, "if that is so, I'll trust your taste as to the music, and your discretion as to the morals. Have the score sent to the copyist."

I hastened at once to Mozart and had not finished telling him the good news when one of the Emperor's lackeys came with a note requesting him to go to the palace at once with the score. He obeyed the royal command and had various pieces performed before the Emperor, who liked them wonderfully well and was, without exaggeration, amazed by them.[3]

Some explanation and correction of this account is in order. That da Ponte, in 1785, "perceived the greatness" of Mozart's genius is by no means certain. We must remember that he was writing forty years after the event, when Mozart's fame had spread to America, where da Ponte was seeking to bolster his own reputation. The secrecy that da Ponte attaches to the composition of the work is a figment of his lively imagination. Even the Salzburg journalist mentioned by Leopold in the letter quoted above "said something about a new opera", when Wolfgang had just begun to write it. In another letter, dated November 11, Leopold reported that Wolfgang, "in order to keep the morning free for composing, . . . is now taking all his pupils in the afternoon, etc." All was not ready in six weeks. Mozart began composing the opera at the end of October 1785 and finished it six months later—on April 29, 1786. The earlier Mozart opera mentioned by the Emperor is probably *Die Entführung aus dem Serail*, which is of course not the only one he had written up to that time. Da Ponte's line of attack was based on either knowledge or sound instinct, for the Emperor, in his memorandum (dated January 31, 1785, and not, therefore, "only a few days before") forbidding a Viennese production of Beaumarchais' play, had added that the censor could permit it to be performed if the offending sections were altered.

Additional information is supplied by another contemporary, Michael Kelly, an Irish tenor living in Vienna, the creator of the roles of Basilio and Don Curzio:

There were three operas on the tapis, one by Regini [Vincenzo Righini], another by Salieri (*The Grotto of Trophonius*), and one by Mozart, by special command of the Emperor . . . These three pieces were nearly ready for representation at the same time, and each composer claimed the right of producing his opera for the first. The contest raised much discord, and parties were formed. The characters of the three men were all very different. Mozart was as touchy as gunpowder, and swore he would put the score of his opera into the fire if it was not produced first; his claim was backed by a strong party: on the contrary, Regini was working like a mole in the dark to get precedence.

---

[3] *Memoirs of Lorenzo da Ponte*, transl. and ed. by L. A. Sheppard, London: Routledge & Kegan Paul Ltd., 1929, pp. 129 ff.

> The third candidate was Maestro di Cappella to the court, a clever shrewd man, possessed of what Bacon called, crooked wisdom, and his claims were backed by three of the principal performers, who formed a cabal not easily put down. Every one of the opera company took part in the contest. I alone was a stickler for Mozart, and naturally enough, for he had a claim on my warmest wishes, from my adoration of his powerful genius, and the debt of gratitude I owed him, for many personal favors.
>
> The mighty contest was put an end to by His Majesty issuing a mandate for Mozart's *Nozze di Figaro,* to be instantly put into rehearsal; and none more than Michael O'Kelly, enjoyed the little great man's triumph over his rivals. . . . I remember at the first rehearsal of the full band, Mozart was on the stage with his crimson pelisse and gold-laced cocked hat, giving the time of the music to the orchestra. Figaro's song, *Non più andrai, farfallone amoroso,* Bennuci [Francesco Benucci] gave, with the greatest animation, and power of voice.
>
> I was standing close to Mozart, who, *sotto voce,* was repeating, Bravo! Bravo! Bennuci; and when Bennuci came to the fine passage, *Cherubino, alla vittoria, alla gloria militar,* which he gave out with Stentorian lungs, the effect was electricity itself, for the whole of the performers on the stage, and those in the orchestra, as if animated by one feeling of delight, vociferated Bravo! Bravo! Maestro. Viva, viva, grande Mozart. Those in the orchestra I thought would never have ceased applauding, by beating the bows of their violins against the music desks. The little man acknowledged, by repeated obeisances, his thanks for the distinguished mark of enthusiastic applause bestowed upon him.[4]

* *
*

La Folle Journée, ou Le Mariage de Figaro is the second of a group of three plays about the same principal characters by Pierre-Augustin Caron de Beaumarchais (1732-99), the first being *Le Barbier de Séville, ou La Précaution Inutile* (1775), and the third, *L'Autre Tartuffe, ou La Mère Coupable* (1792). Beaumarchais, a bold and brilliant man with many irons in the fire (among other things he was instrumental in securing French help for the American colonists in their revolt against England), completed *Le Mariage de Figaro* in 1778. When Louis XVI read the manuscript he exclaimed: "This is detestable, it will never be played!" Apparently the King felt that the very foundations of the social structure in Europe were threatened by the impudent Figaro. Beaumarchais was not a man to take royal censorship meekly, and he enlisted the aid of powerful members of the aristocracy, including several who were close to Queen Marie Antoinette. The affair became a celebrated one in Paris. Private performances were given in the homes of the nobility; eventually the King yielded and the first public performance took place in Paris on April 27, 1784. The play was a resounding success and ran for 68 performances. Two German translations were printed immediately. It was only nine months after the play opened in Paris that Joseph II, as we have seen, felt obliged to place obstacles in the way of its production in German at Vienna.

There was justification for Louis XVI's nervousness. Under the cloak of a gay and witty comedy of intrigue, Beaumarchais poked fun at the dissoluteness of the upper classes and at the legal procedures of the time (with which he had had many unfortunate experiences himself), emphasized the enslavement of the lower orders, and bitterly attacked the power placed

[4] *Reminiscences of Michael Kelly,* London, 1826, I, 257 ff.

in the hands of undeserving men merely because they were born into a certain class of society. The fact that the scene of the play was placed in Spain deceived no one. It was no less an authority than Napoleon who later said that Beaumarchais' play was "the Revolution already in action".

But it was not the political aspect of *Le Mariage de Figaro* that appealed to Mozart. He had never had much interest in politics and his letters are almost bare of references to such matters. Neither the American Revolution nor the French is mentioned once in his correspondence. What attracted him, we must suppose, were the clever and comical convolutions of the complicated plot, in which the victory in the seemingly unequal struggle between the Count and his valet is always about to be won by one or the other antagonist only to be torn out of his grasp by some new crisis. And what must have pleased him above all were the wonderful opportunities for music in this comedy (Beaumarchais had already provided for some songs and dances) and especially for the musical delineation of the fairly numerous and sharply differentiated characters, who, although outgrowths of stock figures of the old Italian *commedia dell' arte*, had achieved in Beaumarchais' hands a freshness and humanity rare in opera librettos of the time.

In making a libretto out of the play, da Ponte did a masterly job. He cut Beaumarchais' cast of sixteen characters down to eleven, telescoped the five acts of the original into four, tightened the more discursive portions of the play, changed the order of some scenes and combined others to make for swifter action and especially to give opportunities for set musical numbers as well as for the great second-act finale. Wherever possible he kept original scenes and, frequently, lines. All the political and many of the satirical social references were deleted. The main lines of Beaumarchais' plot were retained and in some respects the plot was even improved, from the dramaturgical standpoint. Thus, for example, in the play the Countess makes a first, insignificant, appearance towards the end of Act I, but da Ponte keeps her off the stage until she can appear alone at the beginning of Act II. The character of some of the personages is changed. Figaro is still an impertinent rogue, but there is no bitterness in him. The Countess becomes a more sympathetic person and the trace of amorousness in her relation to Cherubino disappears. And so with the other important characters. Through da Ponte's skill and above all through the magic of Mozart's marvelous music all of the characters gain an added dimension of warmth and humanity.

* *
*

The first performance of the opera took place at the Imperial Court Theater in Vienna on May 1, 1786, with the following cast:

Count Almaviva	Stefano Mandini
Countess Almaviva	Luisa Laschi
Susanna	Anna Storace
Figaro	Francesco Benucci
Cherubino	Mme. Bussani
Marcellina	Mme. Mandini
Basilio Don Curzio	Michael Kelly
Bartolo Antonio	Francesco Bussani
Barbarina	Nannina Gottlieb

"At the end of the opera," says Kelly, "I thought the audience would never have done applauding and calling for Mozart, almost every piece was encored, which prolonged it nearly to the length of two operas, and induced the Emperor to issue an order on the second representation, that no piece of music should be encored. Never was anything more complete, than the triumph of Mozart and his *Nozze di Figaro*."[5] It was a short-lived triumph, at least in Vienna. After eight more performances that season it was dropped from the repertory; the success of a new hit—Martín's *Una Cosa Rara*—eclipsed the memory of Mozart's opera and it was not given again in Vienna until three years later.

Meanwhile, however, *Figaro* was performed in Prague in December 1786, "with such success", Leopold reported to his daughter January 12, 1787, "that the orchestra and a company of distinguished connoisseurs and lovers of music sent [Wolfgang] letters inviting him to Prague and also a poem which was composed in his honor". From Prague Mozart wrote to a friend two days later that at a ball he attended "I looked on . . . with the greatest pleasure while all these people flew about in sheer delight to the music of my *Figaro*, arranged for quadrilles and waltzes. For here they talk about nothing but *Figaro*. No opera is drawing like *Figaro*. Nothing, nothing but *Figaro*. Certainly a great honor for me!"[6] Because of this great success, the manager of the Prague Italian opera company commissioned Mozart to write another opera, a commission that resulted in *Don Giovanni*.

Figaro was soon (1787) produced in Germany and quickly became popular there. It was performed in Italy (at Monza) in 1787; in Paris, 1793; London, 1812; New York, 1824; St. Petersburg, 1836; Rio de Janeiro, 1848. Today there is probably no city in which opera is performed that has not seen *Figaro*. It has been given in many languages; Einstein's edition of the Köchel catalogue of Mozart's works lists 14 different translations into German alone.

* *
*

No better brief outline of the plot of the opera can be given than in the words of the author of the play. Here is a first draft, by Beaumarchais himself, of the story of *Le Mariage de Figaro*. It corresponds in almost every detail with da Ponte's libretto and is in fact a better summary of Mozart's opera than of the final version of Beaumarchais' play.

Program of *Le Mariage de Figaro*

Figaro, steward at the castle of Aguas Frescas, has borrowed ten thousand francs from Marceline, housekeeper of the same castle, and has given her a note promising to repay the money at a certain time or to marry her if he should default. Meanwhile, very much in love with Suzanne, Countess Almaviva's young chambermaid, he prepares to marry her; for the Count, himself enamored

[5] Kelly, p. 261. A rugged individualist by the name of Count Karl von Zinzendorf attended the first performance and made a careful note of it in his diary. Here is his comment, in its entirety: "The opera bored me."

[6] Anderson, III, 1343, 1344.

of young Suzanne, has favored this marriage in the hope that a dowry he has promised to give her would enable him to obtain from her in secret her yielding to the *droit du seigneur*, a right that he had renounced for the benefit of his servants when he was married. This little domestic intrigue is conducted on behalf of the Count by the rather unscrupulous Basile, music-master of the castle. But the young and virtuous Suzanne believes herself obliged to apprise her mistress and her betrothed of the Count's gallant intentions, and the Countess, Suzanne, and Figaro band together to foil the plans of the lord of the manor. A small page, beloved by everyone at the castle but mischievous and overheated, like all precocious lads of thirteen or fourteen, slips saucily away from his master and by his liveliness and perpetual thoughtlessness more than once involuntarily places obstacles in the way of the Count's progress, at the same time getting himself into hot water, which leads to some very effective incidents in the piece . . . The Count, finally perceiving that he is being made the victim, but unable to imagine how it is being done, resolves upon vengeance by favoring Marceline's claims. Thus, desperate because he cannot make the young woman his mistress, he tries to marry the old one to Figaro, who is distressed by all this. But at the moment when Almaviva believes himself avenged, when, as first magistrate of Andalusia, he condemns Figaro to marry Marceline that day or pay the ten thousand francs—which Figaro cannot possibly do—, it is revealed that Marceline is Figaro's unknown mother. This ruins all of the Count's plans and he cannot flatter himself that he is either fortunate or avenged. During this time, the Countess, who has not given up the hope of winning back her unfaithful spouse by catching him at fault, has arranged with Suzanne that the latter pretend to grant the Count a rendezvous at last in the garden, and that the wife appear there in place of the mistress. But an unforeseen incident apprises Figaro of the rendezvous granted by his fiancée. Furious because he believes himself deceived, he hides at the appointed spot, in order to surprise the Count with Suzanne. While he is still raging, he is himself pleasantly surprised to discover that the whole affair is only a game between the Countess and her chambermaid for the purpose of fooling the Count; he finally joins in the game good-humoredly; Almaviva, convicted of unfaithfulness by his wife, throws himself at her feet, begs her forgiveness, which she laughingly grants him, and Figaro marries Suzanne.[7]

NATHAN BRODER

NOTE

Hardly two of all the available published scores of *Le Nozze di Figaro* agree with respect to the stage directions. The present edition uses the rather scanty directions in Mozart's manuscript score, augmented with directions from the first edition of da Ponte's libretto, published in Vienna either shortly before or shortly after the first performance of the opera. The only known surviving copy of this fascinating booklet is in the Library of Congress in Washington. Certain pencil markings in an 18th-century hand make it seem likely that this copy belonged to one of the members of the original cast.[8]

The numbering of the scenes has been omitted in the present edition because it varies in the sources and because it is now of little use to performers. The numbers of the set musical pieces have of course been retained. No. 24 (with the preceding recitative of Marcellina) is customarily omitted in performances of the opera.

[7] Eugène Lintilhac, *Histoire générale du théâtre en France*, Paris, n.d., IV, 414-16.

[8] For details, see Siegfried Anheisser, *Die unbekannte Urfassung von Mozarts Figaro*, in *Zeitschrift für Musikwissenschaft*, XV (1933), 301.

INDEX

INDEX *(continued)*

Le Nozze di Figaro
The Marriage of Figaro

Lorenzo da Ponte
English version by
Ruth and Thomas Martin

Wolfgang Amadeus Mozart

Overture

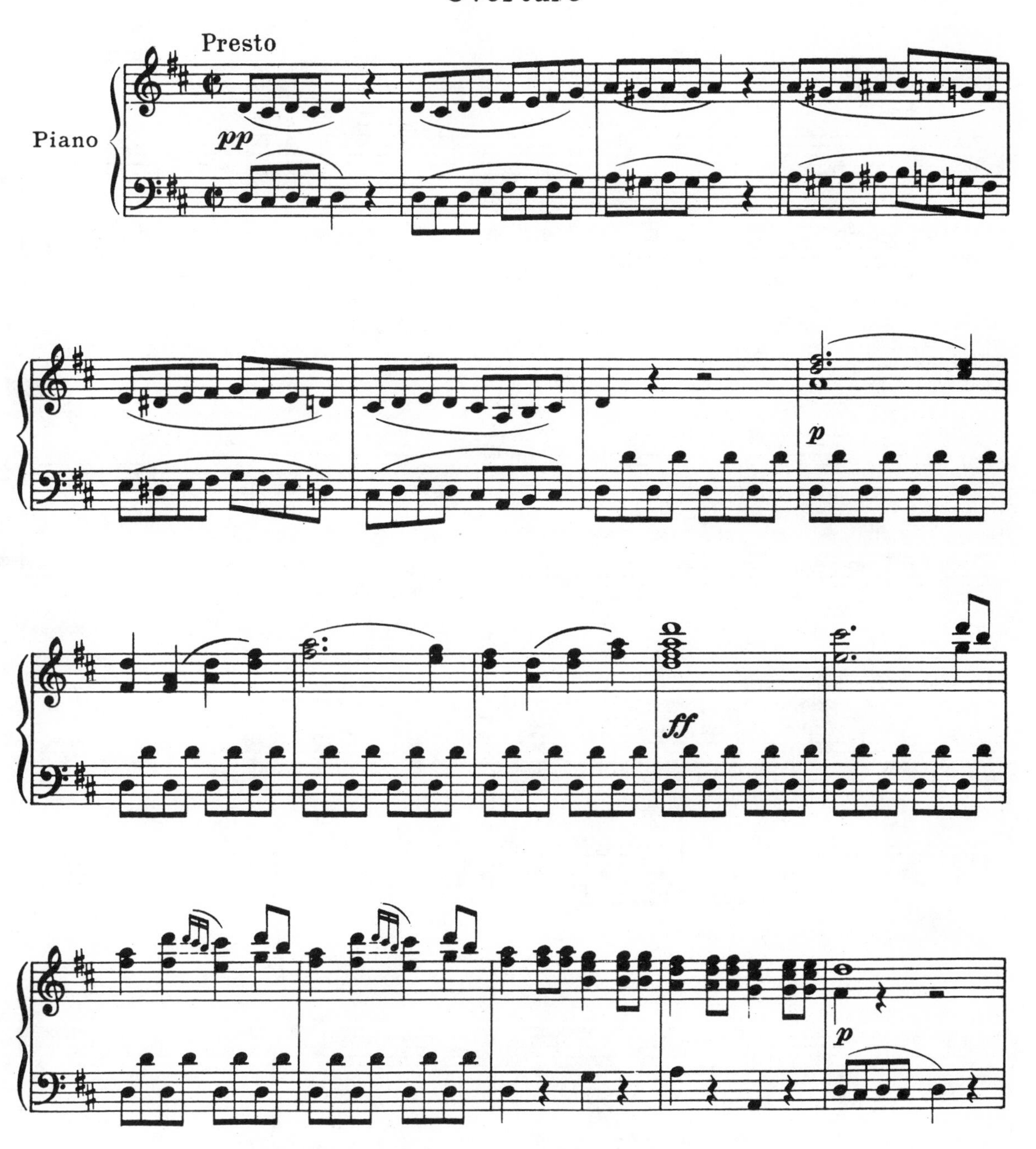

ff
f
p
f
p

f
p
f

fp
fp
fp
fp
fp
fp
p
fp
fp
fp
fp
fp
fp
f
p
f
p

f
f
p

tr
3
3

f
p
f
p
f
p
f
p
f
p
f
p
f
p
pp

p
ff
p

tr
f
fp
p

p
f
p
f
p
f
p
f
p

tr
pp

cresc.
f
tr

tr
tr
[Attacca]

Act I

(Scene: *An incompletely furnished room, with an arm-chair in the middle. Figaro has a ruler in his hand; Susanna is seated at a mirror, trying on a small, flowered hat.)*

No.1. Cinque... dieci...

Seven... fourteen...

Duettino

Figaro and Susanna

p
Figaro (measuring)
Cin - que . . .
Sev - en . . .
die - ci . . .
four - teen . . .
ven - tì . . .
twen - ty . . .
tren - ta...
thir - ty...
tren - ta - se - i . . .
thir - ty - sev - en...

Susanna (looking at herself in the mirror)
quaran - ta - tre... O - ra sì ch'io son con - ten - ta, sem - bra
and for - ty - three... I must say, it's to my lik - ing, just the
mf
p
mfp
fat - to in ver per me, sem - bra fat - to in ver per
ver - y — thing for me, just the ver - y thing for
p
me! Guar - da un po', mio ca - ro Fi - ga - ro, guar - da un
me! Won't you look, my dar - ling Fi - ga - ro, won't you
Cin - que... die - ci...
Sev - en... four - teen...
po', mio ca - ro Fi - ga - ro! Guar - da un po', guar - da un
look, my dar - ling Fi - ga - ro! Turn a - round, turn a -
ven - ti... tren - ta...
twen - ty... thir - ty...

(continuing to look at her reflection in the mirror)
po', guar-da a-des-so il mio cap-pel - lo, guar-da a-des-so il mio cap-
round! Is-n't this a love-ly bon - net? Is-n't this a love-ly
tren - ta-se-i...
thir - ty-sev-en...
pel-lo! Guar-da un po', mio ca-ro
bon-net? Tell me frank-ly, my dear
qua-ran - ta - tre...
and for - ty - three...
Fi - ga-ro, guar-da a-des-so il mio cap - pel-lo, il mio cap-pel-lo, il mio cap-
Fi - ga-ro, do you like me in this bon-net, don't you love the trim-ming
cresc.
Figaro
pel-lo! Sì, mio co - re, or è più bel - lo, sem - bra
on it? Yes, my sweet, the way you've done it, it's a
fp
p
mfp

fat - to in ver_ per_ te, sem - bra fat - to in ver per
pret - ty_ sight to_ see, and it suits you to a
p
Susanna
Guar-da un po', guar-da un po'!
Just look at it! just look at it!
te! Sì, mio co - re, or è più
T! Yes, my sweet-heart, it's ver - y
mfp
mfp
O - ra sì_ ch'io son_ con - ten - ta, o - ra
I must say,_ it's_ to_ my_ lik - ing, ver - y
bel - lo, sì, mio
charm - ing, ver - y
p

sì — ch'io son con - ten - ta, sem - bra fat - to in ver per -
smart and ver - y — strik - ing, just the ver - y — thing for —
co - re, or è — più — bel - lo, sem - bra fat - to in ver per
smart and ver - y — strik - ing, and it suits you to a
mfp
mfp
me, per me, per — me! Ah! il mat - ti - no al - le noz - ze vi -
me, for me, for — me! I have made it my - self for the
te, per - te, per - te! Ah! il mat - ti - no al - le noz - ze vi -
T, to a T, to a T! You have made it your - self for the
p
ci - no, quant' è dol - ce al mio te - ne - ro spo - so, que - sto
wed - ding, as your bride I am plan - ning to wear it, I'm so
ci - no, quant' è dol - ce al tuo te - ne - ro spo - so, que - sto
wed - ding, as my bride you are plan - ning to wear it, I'm so
sf
p
sf
p

bel cap-pel-li - no vez - zo - so, che Su - san - na el-la stes - sa si
hap - py I hard - ly can bear it! What a won - der-ful day that will
bel cap-pel-li - no vez - zo - so, che Su - san - na el-la stes - sa si
hap - py I hard - ly can bear it! What a won - der-ful day that will
p
fe, che Su - san - na el-la stes - sa si fe, Su -
be, what a won - der-ful day that will be! My
fe, che Su - san - na el-la stes - sa si fe, Su-san-na,
be, what a won - der-ful day that will be! Su-san-na,
san-na! el-la stes-sa, che Su - san - na el - la stes - sa si
dar-ling! my be - lov-ed! What a won - der - ful day that will
el - la stes-sa, che Su - san - na el - la stes - sa si
my Su-san-na! What a won - der - ful day that will

fe', stes - sa si fe', stes - sa si
be! Oh, what a day! Oh, what a
fe', stes - sa si fe', stes - sa si
be! Oh, what a day! Oh, what a
f
fe', che Su - san - na el - la stes - sa si
day! What a won - der - ful day, that will
fe', che Su - san - na el - la stes - sa si
day! What a won - der - ful day that will
fe'!
be!
fe'!
be!

Recitative

Susanna and Figaro

(doing the same)
Susanna
chè non puoi far, che pas - si un pò qui! Per - chè non vo - glio;
why not speak out and say what is wrong? I just don't want to.
Figaro
sei tu mio ser-vo, o no? Ma non ca - pis - co, per - chè tan - to ti
Must you know all I'm think - ing? But I can't fath - om why you find it so dis -
Susanna
spia - ce la più co - mo - da stan - za del pa - laz - zo. Per-chio
taste - ful that we're get - ting the best room in the cas - tle. Be -
Figaro
son la Su - san - na, e tu sei paz - zo. Gra - zie, non tan - ti e -
cause I am Su - san - na, and you are stu - pid. Thank you, I like your
lo - gi; guar-da un po - co, se po - tria - si star me-glio in al - tro lo - co.
frank-ness. Look a - round then, and per - haps you can find us bet - ter quar - ters.

No. 2. Se a caso madama la notte ti chiama

Some night if your mistress should ring

Duettino

Figaro and Susanna

f
din, in due pas - si da quel - la puoi gir.
ding, in a wink you could an - swer the call.
f
p
Vien
Sup -
poi l'oc - ca - sio - ne che vuol - mi il pa - dro - ne,
pose I am need - ed to wait on my mas - ter,
che vuol - mi il pa - dro - ne,
to wait on my mas - ter,
f

f
don, don, don, don, in tre sal - ti lo va - do a ser -
dong, dong, dong, dong, I could be there in no time at
f
vir.
all.
p
Susanna
Co - si se il mat - ti - no il ca - ro Con -
Sup - pose your dear mas - ter should send you on an
ti - no, il ca - ro, il ca - ro Con -
er - rand, our dear - est, our gen - er - ous

p
ti - no, din, din, din, din, e ti
mas-ter, ding, ding, ding, ding, on an
p f
man - da tre mi - glia lon - tan, din, din, don,
er - rand some three miles a - way, ding, ding, dong,
p
p
don, don, don, a mia por - ta il
dong, dong, dong, in no time he would
f
p
f
dia - vol lo por - ta ed ec - co in tre sal - ti...
stand in my door - way. Be - fore I could stop him...
Figaro p
Su -
Su -
tr
cresc.
f p
sf p

san - na, pian, pian, Su - san - na, pian, pian, Su -
san - na, hold on, Su - san - na, hold on, Su -
tr
Susanna
Ed ec - co, in tre
While you are on an
san - na, pian, pian, pian, pian,
san - na, no more, no more,
sal - ti, din, din, don,
er - rand, ding, ding, dong,
pian, pian, pian, pian,
hold on, no more,
cresc.

Recit.
p a tempo
don! A - scol - ta! Se u - dir
dong! And fur - ther, I'll tell
pian, pian! Fa pre - sto!
no more! Let's hear it!
f
p colla parte
bra - mi il re - sto, se u - dir bra - mi il re - sto,
you the sto - ry, the whole of the sto - ry,
f
di - scac - cia i so - spet - ti, che tor - to mi
but cast all sus - pi - cions and doubts from your
cresc.
f
Figaro
p
fan. U - dir bra - mo il re - sto, u - dir
mind. I must hear the sto - ry, the whole
p

bra - mo il re - sto, i dub - bi, i so - spet - ti ge -
of the sto - ry, for doubts and sus - pi - cions still
la - re mi fan.
tor - ture my mind.
Susanna
Di - scac - cia i so - spet - ti, i so -
Dis - card all your sil - ly and
spet - ti, i so - spet - ti.
jeal - ous sus - pi - cions.
I dub - bi, i so - spet - ti ge - la - re mi
My doubts and sus - pi - cions still tor - ture my

Di - scac-cia i so - spet-ti, i so - spet-ti, i so -
Dis - card all your sil - ly and jeal - ous sus -
fan, i dub - bi, i so - spet - ti ge - la - re mi
mind, they haunt me and taunt me, my doubts and sus - pi -
spet - ti, di - scac - cia i so - spet - ti che tor - to mi fan, che
pi - cions, dis - card them as ground - less and ver - y un - kind, dis -
fan, i dub - bi, i so - spet - ti ge - la - re mi fan, ge -
cions, my doubts and sus - pi - cions still tor - ture my mind, they
cresc.
tor - to, che tor - to mi fan, che tor -
card them as ver - y un - kind, dis - card
la - re, ge - la - re mi fan, ge - la -
tor - ture, they tor - ture my mind, they tor -
cresc.

p
to, che tor - to mi fan, di -
them as ver - y un - kind, your
p
re, ge - la - re mi fan, ge - la - re mi
ture, they tor - ture my mind, they tor - ture my
tr
scac - cia i dub - bi, i so -
jeal - ous and sil - ly sus -
fan, ge - la - re mi fan, ge - la - re mi
mind, they tor - ture my mind, they tor - ture my
tr
tr
spet - ti!
pi - cions!
fan!
mind!
dim.

Recitative

Susanna and Figaro

Figaro (surprised) Susanna
Di te? Di me me - des - ma, ed ha spe - ran - za ch'al
Not you? You're right the first time, and he is hop - ing that
Figaro
no - bil suo pro - get - to u - ti. - lis - si - ma sia tal vi - ci - nan - za. Bra - vo!
hav - ing us so near him will go far to ad-vance his lit - tle proj - ect. Per - fect!
Susanna
ti - ria - mo a - van - ti! Que - ste le gra - zie son, que - sta la
We're mak - ing head - way. That's why he seems so kind, there - fore so
Figaro
cu - ra ch'e-gli pren-de di te, del-la tua spo-sa. O guar-da un po', che ca-ri-tà pe-
thought-ful in res-pect to the brid-al coup-le's com-fort. Just think of that! Such o-ver-whelm-ing
Susanna
lo - sa! Che - ta - ti, or vie - ne il me - glio; Don Ba - si - lio, mio mae - stro di can - to,
kind-ness! But lis - ten, now comes the best part: Don Ba - si - lio, who teach - es me sing - ing,

e suo fac-to - tum, nel dar-mi la le - zio - ne, mi ri - pe - te o-gni di que-sta can-
acts as his mouth-piece, and dur-ing ev-'ry les - son he keeps harp-ing for - ev - er on the
Figaro
Susanna
zo - ne. Chi! Ba - si - lio! oh, bir - ban - te! E tu cre - de - vi che
sub-ject. Who, Ba - si - lio? How re - volt - ing! Did you im - ag - ine the
Figaro
fos-se la mia do - te mer - to del tuo bel mu - so? Me n'e - ra lu - sin-
Count prom-ised me a dow - ry on the strength of your good looks? I was in-clined to
Susanna
ga - to! Ei la de - sti - na per ot - ten - er da me cer - te mezz'
think so! He wants to bribe me to grant him his feu - dal right as lord and
Figaro
o - re... che il di - rit - to feu - da - le... Co - me! ne' feu - di suo - i non l'ha il
mas - ter on the night of our wed - ding... What? Did he not a - bol - ish that

Susanna
Con - te a - bo - li - to? Eb - ben, o - ra è pen - ti - to, e par che
right when he got mar - ried? He did, but now he's sor - ry, and he would
Figaro
ten - ti ri - scat - tar - lo da me. Bra - vo! mi pia - ce! che ca - ro si - gnor
like to re - store it for me. Would he? Who would - n't! A tru - ly no - ble
(A bell is heard.)
Con - te! Ci vo - gliam di - ver - tir; tro - va - to a - ve - te! Chi
ges - ture! How a - mus - ing in - deed! But I will show him... Who's
Susanna
suo - na? La Con - tes - sa. Ad - dio, ad - di - o, Fi - Fi - Fi - ga - ro
ring - ing? It's the Count - ess. I'll have to an - swer, Fi - Fi - Fi - ga - ro
Figaro
Susanna
(Exit Susanna.)
bel - lo. Co - rag - gio, mio te - so - ro. E tu cer - vel - lo.
dar - ling. Good - bye, my love, be cheer - ful! And you be care - ful!

Figaro (striding forcefully up and down the room, and
Bra-vo, si-gnor pa-dro-ne! O-ra in-co-min-cio
Splen-did, my dear-est mas-ter! Now I'm be-gin-ning
[Moderato]
rubbing his hands)
a ca-pir il mi-ste-ro, e a ve-der schiet-to tut-to il vo-stro pro-
to un-scram-ble this puz-zle and see your pur-pose in its prop-er di-
get-to; a Lon-dra, è ve-ro? Voi mi-
men-sions. We're off to Lon-don, you as
ni-stro, io cor-rie-ro, e la Su-san-na...
en-voy, I as cour-ier, and my Su-san-na...
Andante
[Andante]
se-cre-ta am-ba-scia-tri-ce. Non sa-rà, non sa-rà, Fi-ga-ro il di-ce!
am-bas-sa-dress in se-cret. That shall nev-er be so— Fi-ga-ro has spo-ken!

No. 3. Se vuol ballare

Should my dear master want some diversion

Cavatina

Figaro

Se vuol ve - ni - re
Should he, for in - stance,
nel - la mia scuo - la, la ca - pri - o - la
wish to go danc - ing, he'll face the mu - sic,
le in - se - gne - rò, se vuol ve - ni - re nel - la mia
I'll lead the band. Should he, for in - stance, wish to go
scuo - la, la ca - pri - o - la le in - se - gne - rò, sì,
danc - ing, he'll face the mu - sic, I'll lead the band, yes,

le in - se - gne - rò, sì, le in - se - gne - rò. Sa -
just let him say so, I'll lead the band. And
prò, sa - prò, sa -
then I'll take my
prò, sa - prò, sa - prò, ma pia - no,
cue, with - out a - do, and sly - ly,
pia - no, pia - no, pia - no, pia - no, pia - no, pia - no;
ver - y, ver - y, ver - y, ver - y, ver - y sly - ly,
p
f
p
f
p
fp
fp
fp
fp

me - glio o - gni ar - ca - no
us - ing dis - cre - tion,
dis - si - mu - lan - do sco - prir po - trò.
I shall un - cov - er his se - cret plan.
Presto
L'ar - te scher - men - do, l'ar - te a - do - pran - do,
Sub - tly out - wit - ting, in - no - cent seem - ing,
p
tr
di quà pun - gen - do, di là scher - zan - do,
clev - er - ly hit - ting, plan - ning and schem - ing,

tut - te le mac - chi - ne ro - ve - scie - rò, ro - ve - scie - rò.
I'll get the best of the hyp - o - crite yet, I'll beat him yet!
tr
cresc.
f
p
L'ar - te scher - men - do, l'ar - te a - do - pran - do, di quà pun - gen - do, di là scher - zan - do,
Sub - tly out - wit - ting, in - no - cent seem - ing, clev - er - ly hit - ting, plan - ning and schem - ing,
tut - te le mac - chi - ne ro - ve - scie - rò, tut - te le
teach him a les - son he'll nev - er for - get, teach him a

mac-chi-ne ro - ve-scie - rò, tut - te le mac - chi - ne
les-son he will not for - get, teach him a les - son he'll
p
ro - ve-scie - rò, ro - ve - scie - rò, ro - ve - scie - rò.
nev - er for - get, this time I shall up - set his plan.
p
cresc.
f
[Tempo I°]
Se vuol bal - la - re, si - gnor Con - ti - no,
Should my dear mas - ter want some di - ver-sion,
p staccato
se vuol bal - la - re, si - gnor Con - ti - no,
should my dear ma - ster want some di - ver - sion,

il chi - tar - ri - no le suo - ne - ro, il chi - tar -
I'll play the mu - sic on my guitar, I'll play the
ri - no le suo - ne - rò, sì, le suo - ne -
mu - sic on my gui - tar, yes, on my gui -
rò, sì, le suo - ne - rò.
tar, yes, on my gui - tar!
Presto
(Exit.)
f

Recitative

Bartolo and Marcellina

rir, con-vien con ar - te im - pun - ti - gliar - la a ri - fiu - ta - re il Con - te;
clear. If we suc-ceed in mak - ing Su - san - na re-ject the Count's ad-vanc-es,
e - gli per ven - di - car - si pren - de - rà il mio par - ti - to, e Fi - ga - ro co -
then, for the sake of venge - ance, he will fa - vor our proj - ect, and Fi - ga - ro will
(He takes the contract from Marcellina.)
Bartolo
sì fia mio ma - ri - to. Be - ne, io tut - to fa - rò; sen - za ri -
thus be - come my hus - band! Splen - did, I'll do all I can, spar-ing no
ser - ve, tut - to a me pa - le - sa - te. (A-vrei pur gu - sto di dar in
ef - fort to ac-com - plish your ob - ject. (How I would love to ar-range a
[Exit Marcellina.]
mo-glie la mia ser - va an - ti - ca a chi mi fe - ce un dì ra - pir l'a-mi-ca.)
match for my old ser-vant Mar - cel - li - na with the rogue who foiled my mar-riage to Ro - si - na!)

No. 4. La vendetta

Taking vengeance

Aria

Bartolo

sez-za, è o-gnor vil - tà, è bas-sez-za, è o-gnor vil-
hav-ing in bas - est form, that's be-hav-ing just like a
sfp
sfp
sfp
sfp
tà, è o-gnor vil - tà. Coll' a-stu-zia, coll' ar-gu-zia,
worm, a fright - ened worm! Do it my way, take the sly way.
sfp
f
p
col giu-di-zio, col cri-te-rio, si po-treb-be,
Spread con-fu-sion and dis-trac-tion. Give them ac-tion,
f
p
sfp
sfp
sfp
sfp
si po-treb-be, coll' a-stu-zia, coll' ar - gu-zia, col giu-di-zio, col cri-
give them ac-tion. I will show you how to func-tion, us-ing strat-e-gy and

te - rio, si po - treb - be, si po - treb - be, si po - treb - be, si po -
unc - tion, show no pit - y, no com - punc - tion, and be - fore they knew what
cresc.
f
treb - be, il fat - to'e se - rio, il fat - to'e se - rio, il fat - to'e
hit them, you will out - wit them,you will out - wit them,you will out -
sf
p
3
se - rio. Ma cre - de - te, si fa - rà,
wit them! Take my word, it can be done,
ma cre - de - te, si fa - rà.
and the case can still be won.

Se tut-to il co-di-ce do-ves-si vol-ge-re, se tut-to
Al-ways pro-ceed-ing with ut-most le-gal-i-ty, I shall dis-
l'in-di-ce do-ves-si leg-ge-re, con un e-qui-vo-co, con un si-
cov-er a fine tech-ni-cal-i-ty, I shall e-quiv-o-cate, ar-gue, and
no-ni-mo, qual-che gar-bu-glio si tro-ve-rà, se tut-to il
lit-i-gate, un-til a loop-hole I can pro-duce. I have a-
co-di-ce do-ves-si vol-ge-re, se tut-to l'in-di-ce do-ves-si
bil-i-ty, men-tal a-gil-i-ty, le-gal fa-cil-i-ty, and ver-sa-

leg - ge - re, con un e - qui - vo - co, con un si - no - ni - mo, qual - che gar -
til - i - ty. With my ex - per - ience and in - fal - li - bil - i - ty, an - y op -
bu - glio si tro - ve - rà,
po - nent sure - ly will lose.
qual - che gar - bu - glio
Oh, what con - fu - sion
sfp
si tro - ve - rà, si tro - ve - rà!
I shall pro - duce, I shall pro - duce!
sfp
Tut - ta Si - vi - glia co - no - sce Bar - to - lo,
All of the cit - y knows Doc - tor Bar - to - lo
f
p

il bir - bo Fi - ga-ro vin - to sa - rà; tut - ta Si - vi - glia
as for that Fi - ga-ro, I'll cook his goose; all of the cit - y
f
p
f
p
co - no - sce Bar - to - lo, il bir - bo Fi - ga-ro
knows Doc - tor Bar - to - lo— as for that Fi - ga-ro,
f
p
p
f
vin - to sa - rà, il bir - bo Fi - ga-ro vin - to sa -
I'll cook his goose; as for that Fi - ga-ro, I'll cook his
p
rà, il bir - bo Fi - ga-ro vin - to sa - rà,
goose, as for that Fi - ga-ro, I'll cook his goose,
cresc.
f

vin - to sa - rà,
I'll cook his goose,
vin - to sa - rà,
I'll cook his goose,
(Exit.)
vin - to sa - rà.
I'll cook his goose.

Recitative

Marcellina and Susanna

(Marcellina enters; then Susanna, with a night-cap, a ribbon, and a dressing-gown.)

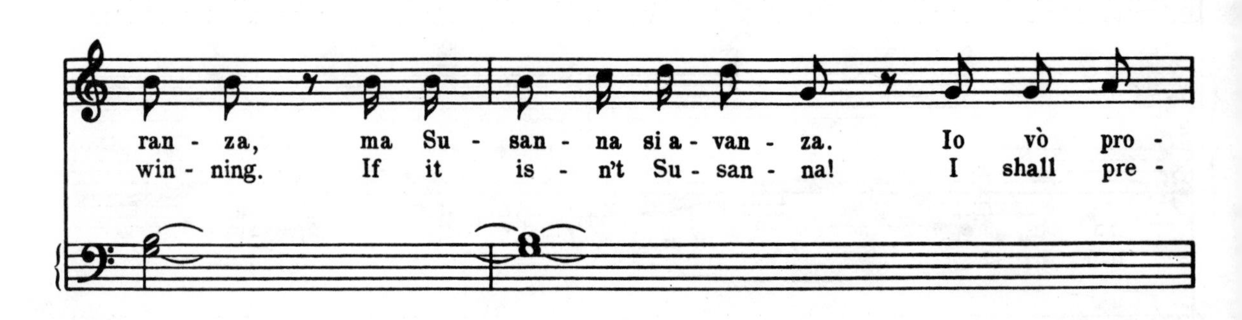

Marcellina
vel - la.) Ma da Fi - ga - ro al - fi - ne non può me - glio spe -
me.) Af - ter all, from a Fi - ga - ro one can't real - ly ex -
Susanna
rar - si: "l'ar - gent fait tout." (Che lin - gua! man - co
pect much, but "mon - ey talks." (Old spin - ster! It's too
Marcellina
ma - le, ch'o-gnun sa quan - to va - le.) Bra - va! que - sto è giu -
bad that she could not find a hus - band!) Real - ly! I can't im -
di - zio! Con que - gli oc - chi mo - de - sti, con quell' a - ria pie -
ag - ine what he sees in this fe - male. She is all skin and
(Both are about to leave, but meet at the door.)
Susanna
Marcellina
to - sa! E po - i... (Me-glio è par - tir.) (Che ca - ra spo - sa!)
bones! I wish I... How do you do? How nice to see you!

No.5. Via resti servita

To greet you, my lady

Duettino

Marcellina and Susanna

(curtsying)
can - te.
treme - ly.
No, no, toc-ca a lei!
No, no, you go first!
Marcellina (curtsying)
(curtsying)
No, pri-ma a lei toc - ca.
Please en - ter be - fore me!
No, pri-ma a lei
I beg you, ig -
(curtsying)
(curtsying)
No, no, toc-ca a lei.
No, no, you go first!
Io so i do-ver
Your no - ble po -
(curtsying)
toc - ca.
nore me!
Io so i do-ver mie - i, so i do-ver
I know my po - si - tion, bow to tra -
mie - i, so i do-ver mie - i, non fo in - ci - vil - tà, io so i do-ver
si - tion, fine and pa - tri - cian, in - spires — re - spect. I know my po -
mie - i, so i do-ver mie - i, non fo in - ci - vil - tà,
di - tion, fine and pa - tri - cian, with all due re - spect.

mie-i, so i do-ver mie-i, so i do-ver mie-i, non fo in-ci-vil-
si-tion, bow to tra-di-tion, and my am-bi-tion is be-ing cor-
io so i do-ver mie-i, so i do-ver mie-i, non fo in-ci-vil-
I know my po-si-tion, bow to tra-di-tion with all due re-
tà.
rect.
Marcellina (curtsying)
tà.
La spo-sa no-vel-la!
spect.
The bride of the hour!
Susanna (curtsying)
La da-ma d'o-no-re!
A la-dy of sta-tion!
Marcellina (curtsying)
Del Con-te la
The Count's lit-tle
bel-la!
flow'r!
Susanna (curtsying)
Di Spa-gna l'a-mo-re!
The pride of the na-tion!
Marcellina
I
Her

Susanna
L'a - bi - to! l'e -
Dig - ni - fied! Ma -
me - ri - ti! il po - sto!
at - ti - tude! Her pos - es!
tà!
ture!
(infuriated)
Per Bac - co! pre - ci - pi - to, se an - cor, se an - cor re - sto
I swear I shall fly at her in one, in one min - ute
f
p
(mockingly)
Si - bil - la de - cre - pi - ta da ri - der mi fa.
De - crep - it old bat - tle - ax, I'll set - tle your score.
(curtsying)
quà! Via re - sti ser -
more! I praise your de -

(curtsying)
Non so - no sì ar - di - ta, ma - da - ma pic -
And I, your ex - pe - rience and broad rep - u -
vi - ta, ma - da - ma bril - lan - te.
port-ment with-out re - ser - va - tion!
cresc.
f
p
(curtsying)
can - te.
ta - tion!
La da - ma d'o -
The belle of the
Marcellina (curtsying)
La spo - sa no - vel - la!
So young and so pret - ty!
cresc.
(curtsying)
no - re!
cit - y!
Di Spa - gna l'a -
The true Span-ish
(curtsying)
Del Con - te la bel - la!
What dis - tance be - tween us!
p
cresc.

mo - re!
Ve - nus!
L'a - bi - to!
Dur - a - ble!
I me - ri - ti!
So in - no-cent!
il
So
p
l'e - tà!
So old!
(infuriated)
po - sto!
sim - ple!
Per Bac - co! pre - ci - pi - to, se an-
How dare she make fun of me, it
f
p
(mockingly)
l'e - tà, l' - tà, l'e - tà,
So old, so old, so old!
cor, se an-cor re - sto quà,
is, it is a dis - grace!
per Bac - co! pre -
How dare she make
cresc.
f
p

(mockingly)
Si-bil - la de-cre-pi-ta, da ri - der, da ri - der mi
De-crep - it old bat-tle-ax, I'll laugh right in her
ci-pi-to, per Bac - co! pre-ci - pi-to, se an-cor re-sto
fun of me! How dare she make fun of me, it is a dis-
cresc.
f
fa, Si - bil - la de-cre-pi-ta, da
face! De-crep - it old bat-tle-ax, I'll
quà, per Bac - co! pre-ci - pi-to, per Bac - co! pre-
grace, how dare she make fun of me, how dare she make
p
cresc.
ri - der, da ri - der mi fa, Si-bil - la de-cre-pi-ta, da ri-der mi
laugh right in her face, de-crep - it old bat-tle-ax, I'll laugh in her
ci-pi-to, se an-cor re-sto quà, per Bac-co! pre-ci-pi-to, se an-cor re-sto
fun of me, it is a dis-grace, how dare she make fun of me, it is a dis-
f
p

fa, Si - bil - - la de - cre - pi - ta, da ri - der mi
face, de - crep - - it old bat - tle - ax, I'll laugh in her
quà, per Bac - co! pre - ci - pi - to, se an - cor re - sto
grace, how dare she make fun of me, it is a dis -
fa, da ri - der mi fa, da ri - der mi fa.
face, I'll laugh in her face, I'll laugh in her face!
(Exit Marcellina angrily.)
quà, se an - cor re - sto quà, se an - cor re - sto quà.
grace, it is a dis - grace, it is a dis - grace!
3
cresc.
f

Recitative

Susanna and Cherubino

(anxiously)
gra-zia non m'in-ter-ce-de, io va-do vi-a, io non ti ve-do più, Su-san-na
can-not ob-tain my par-don, I have to leave and won't see you a-gain, my dear Su-
Susanna
mi-a! Non ve-de-te più me! bra-vo! ma dun-que non
san-na! You won't see me a-gain? how dread-ful! But I al-ways
Cherubino
più per la Con-tes-sa, se-cre-ta-men-te il vo-stro cor so-spi-ra? Ah! che
thought it was the Count-ess who was the ob-ject of your se-cret af-fec-tion! Ah, my
trop-po ri-spet-to el-la m'in-spi-ra! Fe-li-ce te, che puo-i ve-der-la quan-do
la-dy is much too high a-bove me! Oh, luck-y you, you may al-ways see her when you
vuo-i, che la ve-sti il mat-ti-no, che la se-ra la spo-gli, che le
want to, you dress her each morn-ing, you un-dress her each eve-ning, you may

(with a sigh)
met-ti gli spil-lo - ni, i mer-let - ti... ah! se in tuo lo - co... cos' hai
fas-ten all her pins, tie her rib - bons... Were I in your place... What is
Susanna (imitating Cherubino)
lì? Dim-mi un po - co. Ah il va - go na-stro, e la not-tur-na cuf - fia di co-
that? Let me see it! Ah, that is one of her fa - vor-ite rib - bons, and be-
Cherubino
(snatching the ribbon from her)
ma - re sì bel - la. Deh dam - me - lo, so-rel - la, dam-me-lo, per pie -
longs to her night-cap. Oh, give it to me, Su-san - na, please, you must let me
Susanna
(trying to get it back)
Cherubino
(circling the chair)
tà! Pre - sto quel na - stro. O ca - ro, o bel - lo, o for-tu - na - to
see! What are you do - ing? O sweet-est, o love - liest, o most di-vine of
(covering the ribbon with kisses)
Susanna (following him, but then stopping, as though she were exhausted)
na-stro! Io non te'l ren - de - rò che col - la vi - ta! Cos' è quest' in - so -
rib-bons! Not for the whole wide world will I re - turn it! How dare you take that

Cherubino
len - za? Eh via, sta che - ta! In ri - com - pen - sa po - i que - sta
rib - bon? Don't get ex - cit - ed! I'll give you my new love - song in ex -
Susanna
Cherubino
mia can - zo - net - ta io ti vò da - re. E che ne deb - bo fa - re? Leg - gi - la al - la pa -
change. That will make the bar - gain e - ven. What shall I do with love-songs? Sing it to the
dro - na; leg - gi - la tu me - des - ma, leg - gi - la a Bar - ba -
Count - ess, sing it to your - self, sing it to Bar - ba -
(in an ecstasy of joy)
ri - na, a Mar - cel - li - na... leg - gi - la ad o - gni don - na del pa -
ri - na, to Mar - cel - li - na, sing it to all the la - dies in the
Susanna
laz - zo! Po - ve - ro Che - ru - bin, sie - te voi paz - zo!
cas - tle! You must have lost your mind, poor Che - ru - bi - no!

No. 6. Non so più cosa son, cosa faccio

I can't give you a good explanation

Aria

Cherubino

don - na mi fa pal - pi - tar, o - gni don - na mi
trem - ble with plea - sure and pain, makes me trem - ble with
p
mf
p
fa pal - pi - tar. So - lo ai no - mi d'a-mor, di di -
plea - sure and pain. When of love there is mere - ly a
p
cresc.
let - to, mi si tur - ba, mi s'al - te-ra il pet - to,
men - tion, I am spell-bound and rapt with at - ten - tion.
e a par - la - re mi sfor - za d'a - mo - re
I weave ro - manc - es and day-dreams to - geth - er,

un de - si - o, un de - si - o ch'io non
filled with long-ing, filled with long - ing I
pos - so spie - gar, un de - si - o, un de -
can - not ex - plain, filled with long - ing, filled with
si - o ch'io non pos - so spie - gar.
long - ing I can - not ex - plain.
Non so
If I
più co - sa son, co - sa fac - cio, or di fo - co, o - ra so - no di
knew what it is I'd con - fess it, but I am at a loss to ex -
f
p

ghiac-cio, o-gni don-na can-giar di co-lo-re, o-gni
press it, yet I know that it al-ways ex-cites me, that it
f
p
don-na mi fa pal-pi-tar, o-gni don-na mi_
thrills me a-gain and a-gain, that it thrills me a-
mf
p
fa pal-pi-tar, o-gni don-na mi fa pal-pi-
gain and a-gain, that it thrills me a-gain and a-
mf
p
tar. Par-lo d'a-mor ve-
gain. Love is my in-spi-

glian - do, par - lo d'a - mor so -
ra - tion, on - ly con - sid - er -
gnan - do, all' ac - qua, all'om - bra, ai mon - ti, ai fio - ri, all'er - be, ai
a - tion. In riv - ers, woods, and flow - ers, I feel its mag - ic
fp
fon - ti, all' e - co, all' a - ria, ai ven - ti, che il suon de' va - ni ac -
stream - ing, a - wake, a - sleep, and dream - ing. In gen - tle winds and
fp
f
p
cen - ti, por - ta - no via con se, por - ta - no
show - ers, I hear its mel - low tone, I hear its
cresc.
f
colla voce
p

via con se. Par-lo d'a-mor ve-glian - do,
mel - low tone. Love is my con-ver - sa - tion,
par-lo d'a-mor so - gnan - do, all' ac-qua, all' om - bra,
theme with-out var - i - a - tion, I tell my love - song
ai mon-ti, ai fio-ri, all' er-be, ai fon-ti, all'
to glens and moun-tains, to riv-ers and foun-tains, to
e-co, all' a - ria, ai ven - ti, che il suon de' va-ni ac-cen - ti,
moon and stars in heav - en. The gen-tle breez-es ech - o
cresc.
f
p
cresc.

por - ta - no via con se,
my ev - 'ry word and tone,
f
colla voce
p
por - ta - no via con
my ev - 'ry word and
Adagio
se. E se non ho chi m'o - da, e
tone. And if no one will lis - ten... and
fast
Tempo I
se non ho chi m'o - da, par - lo d'a - mor con
if no one will lis - ten, then I will talk a -
cresc.
me, con me, par - lo d'a - mor con me.
lone of love, talk to my - self a - lone.
p
f

Recitative

Cherubino, Susanna, Count, and Basilio

Susanna (timidly)
rò; di con-dur me-co Fi-ga-ro de-sti-na-i. Si-gnor, se o-
Lon-don, and I ar-ranged for Fi-ga-ro to go with me. If I dared
Count (rising)
sas-si— Par-la, par-la, mia ca-ra, e con quel drit-to ch'og-gi pren-di su
ask you—Ask me, ask me, my dar-ling, and with that right you ex-ert o-ver
(tenderly, and trying to take her hand again)
Susanna
me, fin-chè tu vi-vi chie-di, im-po-ni, pre-scri-vi. La-scia-te-mi, si-
me, now and al-ways, ask me, com-pel me, com-mand me! I do not wish that
(angrily)
gnor, drit-ti non pren-do, non ne vò, non ne in-ten-do.
right, I ask no priv-i-lege, I don't want to ex-ert it;
Count
Oh, me in-fe-li-ce! Ah no, Su-san-na, io ti vò far fe-
I'm so un-hap-py! No, no, Su-san-na, I want you to be

(as above)
li - ce! Tu ben sai quan-to io t'a - mo; a te Ba-si - lio tut - to già
hap - py! You must know how much I love you; I'm sure Ba - si - lio told you al -
dis - se. Or sen - ti, se per po - chi mo - men - ti me - co in giar -
read - y! Now lis - ten, if you on - ly con - sent to meet me to -
din sull' im-bru-nir del gior - no, ah per que - sto fa - vo - re io pa - ghe - rei.
night in the gar-den of the cas - tle, I will am - ply re - pay you for this fa - vor.
Basilio
(offstage)
E - u - sci - to po - co fa.
He left not long a - go.
Count
Chi par - la?
Ba - si - lio!
Susanna
O De - i!
Good Heav - ens!
Count
E - sci, ed al - cun non en - tri.
Hur - ry, don't let him en - ter.
Susanna (very agitated)
Ch'io vi la - sci quì so - lo?
I should leave you a - lone here?
Basilio (still offstage)
Da ma - da - ma sa - rà,
He can't be ver - y far, per -

Count (pointing to the chair)
Susanna
va - do a cer - car - lo. Quì die - tro mi por - rò. Non vi ce -
haps with the Count - ess. I'll step be - hind this chair. No, that's too
Count
Susanna
(The Count
la - te. Ta - ci, e cer - ca ch'ei par - ta. Ohi - mè! che fa - te!
risk - y. Qui - et, get rid of him quick - ly. Oh, Lord, how aw - ful!
tries to hide behind the arm-chair; Susanna stands between him and Cherubino; the Count draws her
Basilio (Enters.)
Su - san - na, il ciel vi sal - vi! A - vre - ste a ca - so ve - du - to il
Su - san - na, Heav - en bless you! Do you by chance know where the
gently away; meanwhile the page passes in front of the chair and crouches in it; Susanna covers
Susanna
Basilio
Con - te? E co - sa de - ve far me - co il Con - te? A - ni - mo, u - sci - te. A - spet -
Count is? And what on earth should the Count do here? Go now, I'm bus - y. Just a
him with the dressing-gown.)
Susanna
ta - te, sen - ti - te, Fi - ga - ro di lui cer - ca. (Oh cie - lo!)
min - ute, it seems that Fi - ga - ro wants to see him. The Count,

Count
ei cer - ca chi, do - po voi, più l'o - dia. (Ve - diam co - me mi
the one man who hates him more than you do? (Let's see how he will
Basilio
ser - ve.) Io non ho mai nel - la mo - ral sen - ti - to ch'u - no ch'a - ma la mo - glie o -
serve me.) That is not so. There is no such con - clu - sion, that if one loves the wife, one
Susanna
di il ma - ri - to, per dir che il Con - te v'a - ma. Sor - ti - te, vil mi -
must hate the hus - band. In fact, my mas - ter loves you. Get out of here this
(resentfully)
ni - stro dell' al - trui sfre - na - tez - za: io non ho d'uo - po del - la
min - ute with your hints and sug - ges - tions. I have no in - t'rest in your
Basilio
vo - stra mo - ra - le, del Con - te, del suo a - mor. Non c'è al - cun
lec - tures on mor - als, in your mas - ter, in his love. Don't take it

ma - le. Ha cia-scun i suoi gu - sti. Io mi cre - de - a che pre-fe-rir do-
that way. I don't mean to of-fend you. I was just think - ing that you would pre-
ve-ste per a-man - te, co-me fan tut-te quan - te, un si-gnor li - be-ral, pru-den-te, e
fer the type of lov - er which most wo-men ad - mire, a lord who is lib-er - al and
Susanna (anxiously) Basilio
sag - gio, a un gio - vi - na - stro, a un pag - gio. A Che-ru - bi - no? A Che-ru-
pru - dent, to a young pip-squeak, a page - boy. Not Che-ru - bi - no? Yes, Che-ru-
bi - no, Che-ru-bin d'a - mo - re, ch'og - gi sul far del gior - no pas-seg-
bi - no, Che-ru-bin the Cu - pid, who ear - li - er this morn - ing was
Susanna (forcefully)
gia - va qui in - tor - no per en - trar. Uom ma-li - gno, un' im-po-stu-ra è
prowl-ing near your door, try-ing to en-ter. You're a vil - lain, who tells ma - li - cious

Basilio
que - sta. Èun ma-li - gno con voi, chi ha gli oc-chi in te - sta? E
false-hoods! To have eyes in one's head, is that ma - li - cious? For
quel-la can-zo-net - ta, di - temi in con-fi - den-za, io so-no a-mi - co, ed al-
in-stance, this love-song, tell me, just be - tween us, I can be trust - ed, and will
Susanna (in consternation)
trui nul-la di - co, è per voi, per ma-da - ma? (Chi dia-vol gliel' ha
breathe it to no one. . . is it for you or the Count-ess? (Who the dev-il could have
Basilio
det - to?) A pro-po - si - to, fi - glia, in-stru - i - te-lo me - glio.
told him?) A pro-pos, my dear girl, you should train him much bet - ter.
E - gli la guar-da a ta-vo-la sì spes - so, e con ta-le im-mo-de-stia
When he serves at ta - ble, he gaz-es at the Count-ess with such ob - vi-ous long-ing

che s'il Con-te s'ac-cor-ge, e sul tal pun-to, sa-pe-te, e-gli è u-na
that if the Count should take no-tice you can im-ag-ine, in that case, what's bound to
Susanna
be-stia. Scel-le-ra-to! e per-chè an-da-te voi tai men-zo-gne spar-
hap-pen. Oh, you li-ar! Have you noth-ing more to do than to spread vi-cious
Basilio
gen-do? Io! che in-giu-sti-zia! Quel che com-pro io ven-do, a
gos-sip? I! You're mis-tak-en, I just sell what I pur-chase, I
quel che tut-ti di-co-no, io non ci ag-giun-go un pe-lo.
ech-o what they all say, not add-ing in the slight-est.
Count (Steps forward.)
Basilio
Susanna
Co-me! che di-con tut-ti? Oh bel-la! Oh cie-lo!
Real-ly! What are they say-ing? (De-light-ful!) Ah, Heav-ens!

No. 7. Cosa sento! Tosto andate

That's the limit! Go this minute!

Terzetto

Count, Basilio, and Susanna

son qui giun - to; per - do - na - te, o mio si -
was my sto - ry, just a ru - mor, with - out a
Susanna
gnor. Che ru - i - na! me me - schi - na! son' op - pres - sa dal do -
doubt. We'll be ru - ined by the scan - dal if this gos - sip gets a -
lor!
bout!
Basilio
In mal pun - to
How ill - cho - sen
Count
To - sto an - da - te, an - da - te,
Don't de - lay an - y long - er,
f
p

Che ru - i - na!
This is aw - ful!
son qui giun - to, per - do - na - te, o
was my sto - ry, just a ru - mor, with -
e scac - cia - te il se - dut - tor.
go and throw the scoun - drel out.
f
(half fainting)
Me me - schi - na! me me - schi - na! Son' op -
What will hap - pen! Heav - en help us! I am
mio si - gnor.
out a doubt.
sf
p
pres - sa dal do - lor, son' op - pres - sa dal do -
feel - ing ver - y faint, I am feel - ing ver - y

lor.
faint.
Basilio (supporting her)
Ah! già svien la po - ve - ri - na!
Ah! poor girl, her strength is fail - ing!
Count (supporting her)
Ah! già svien la po - ve - ri - na!
Ah! poor girl, her strength is fail - ing!
Co - me, oh Di - o! le bat - te il
We must help her, re - vive her
Co - me, oh Di - o! le bat - te il
We must help her, re - vive her
cor, co - me, oh Di - o! le bat - te il
fast, or, good Lord, she might not
cor, co - me, oh Di - o! le bat - te il
fast, or, good Lord, she might not
cresc.
p

cor, co - me, oh Di - o! le bat - te il cor.
last, or, good Lord, she might not last.
cor, co - me, oh Di - o! le bat - te il cor.
last, or, good Lord, she might not last.
cresc.
p.
Basilio
(approaching the arm-chair to sit down in it)
Pian, pian - in su que - sto seg - gio.
Let us put her in this arm - chair.
tr
Susanna
(recovering)
(repulsing them both)
Do - ve so - no? Co - sa veg - gio! Che in - so -
Ah, where am I? Am I dream - ing? You in -
tr
cresc.
len - za! an - da - te fuor, an - da - te fuor, an - da - te fuor!
sult me, go a - way, leave me a - lone, leave me a - lone!
f
p
cresc.
f

Basilio (maliciously)
Sia - mo quì per a - iu - tar - vi, è si -
We are on - ly here to help you, I as -
Count
Sia - mo quì per a - iu - tar - vi, non tur -
We are on - ly here to help you, I as -
p
p
cu - ro il vo - stro o - nor, è si - cu - ro il
sure you, we meant no harm, I as - sure you, we
bar - ti, o mio te - sor, non tur - bar - ti, o
sure you, we meant no harm, I as - sure you, we
p
cresc.
cresc.
vo - stro o - nor, è si - cu - ro il vo - stro o - nor.
meant no harm, I as - sure you, we meant no harm.
mio te - sor, non tur - bar - ti, o mio te - sor.
meant no harm, I as - sure you, we meant no harm.
p
sfp
cresc.

Basilio
(to the Count)
Ah, del pag-gio, quel che ho det-to, e-ra so-lo un
What I told you was a ru-mor, mere sus-pi-cion, with
Susanna
mio so-spet-to. È un' in-si-dia, u-na per-fi-dia, non cre-
no foun-da-tion. He is vi-cious and ma-li-cious; it's a
p
cresc.
de-te all' im-po-stor, non cre-de-te all' im-po-stor, all' im-po-
lie, it is not true, it's a lie, it is not true, it is not
f
stor, all' im-po-stor!
true, it is not true!
Count
Par-ta, par-ta il da-me-ri-no,
Or-der him to leave the cit-y!
f
p

Susanna
Po - ve - ri - no!
What a pit - y!
Po - ve -
What a
Basilio
Po - ve - ri - no!
What a pit - y!
Po - ve -
What a
par - ta, par - ta il da - me - ri - no!
Or - der him to leave the cit - y!
f
p
ri - no!
pit - y!
ri - no!
pit - y!
(ironically)
Po - ve - ri - no! po - ve - ri - no! ma da
What a pit - y! what a pit - y! I have
Co - me?
Caught him?
Che?
How?
Che?
How?
me sor - pre - so an - cor!
caught him once be - fore!

Co - me?
Real - ly?
Che?
Where?
Co - me?
Did you?
Co - me?
Real - ly?
Che!
Where?
Recit.
Da tua cu - gi - na,
At Bar - ba - ri - na's,
Recit.
p
Count
l'u - scio jer tro - vai rin - chiu - so, pic - chio,
yes - ter - day, I went to see An - to - nio, I knocked,
m'a - pre Bar - ba - ri - na pau - ro - sa fuor dell' u - so,
Bar - ba - ri - na o - pened, and looked ex - treme - ly ner - vous.
io, dal mu - so in - so - spet - ti - to, guar - do, cer - co in o - gni si - to.
I be - gan to grow sus - pi - cious and ex - am - ined ev - 'ry cor - ner.
f

a tempo
Ed al - zan - do, pian, pia - ni - no, il tap - pe - to al
When I gent - ly drew the cov - er from the ta - ble I
p a tempo
(Showing how he found the page, he lifts the dressing-
ta - vo - li - no, ve - do il pag - gio.
found be - neath it Che - ru - bi - no!
p
Susanna (agitated)
Ah! cru - de stel - le!
Ah, this is aw - ful!
gown from the chair and discovers Cherubino.)
(astonished)
Ah! co - sa veg - gio!
Ha! What does this mean?
Susanna
Ac - ca -
Noth - ing
Basilio (laughing sardonically)
Ah! me - glio an - co - ra!
Ah, this is price - less!
Count
O - ne - stis - si - ma si - gno - ra!
Now at last my eyes are o - pen!
pp

der non può di peg-gio.
Giu-sti
worse than this could hap-pen!
This af-
Or ca-pi-sco co-me va!
Now I see how mat-ters stand!
Dei, che mai sa-rà!
Giu-sti Dei,
fair is out of hand!
This af-fair
Basilio
Co-sì fan tut-te le bel-le, non c'è al-
That's the way all wo-men do it, they will
Or ca-pi-sco
Now I see how
cresc.
che mai sa-rà! ac-ca-der non può di peg-gio, ah,
is out of hand. Noth-ing worse than this could hap-pen, ah,
cu-na no-vi-tà,
co-sì
nev-er show their hand.
That's the
co-me va,
o-ne-stis-si-
mat-ters stand.
Now at last my
f
p
cresc.

no! ah, no! giu - sti Dei, che mai sa - rà, che mai sa -
no! ah, no! This af - fair is out of hand; how will this
fan tut - te_ le_ bel - le, non c'è al - cu - na_ no - vi -
way all wo - men do it, they will nev - er_ show their
ma_ si - gno - ra! or ca - pi - sco co - me
eyes_ are o - pen, now I see_ how mat - ters
f

rà! ac - ca - der non può di peg - gio,
end? Noth - ing worse than this could hap - pen,
tà, co - sì fan tut - te le bel - le,
hand. That's the way all wo - men do it,
va, o - ne - stis - si - ma si - gno - ra,
stand. Now at last___ my eyes are o - pen,
p

giu - sti Dei, — che — mai sa - rà!
no one knows how — this will end.
(to the Count, with malice)
non c'è al - cu - na — no - vi - tà. Ah, del pag - gio
they will nev - er — show their hand. What I told you
or ca - pi - sco — co - me va!
now I see — how — mat - ters stand.
cresc.
p
quel che ho det - to, e - ra so - lo un mio so -
was a ru - mor, mere sus - pi - cion with no foun -

Ac - ca-der non può di peg-gio, ah, no, ah, no! giu - sti
Noth - ing worse than this could hap-pen, ah, no, ah, no! No one
spet-to. Co - sì fan tut-te le bel-le,
da-tion. That's the way all wo-men do it,
O - ne - stis - si - ma si - gno - ra,
Now at last my eyes are o - pen,
cresc.
f

Dei, che mai sa - rà, che mai sa - rà! Ac - ca -
knows how this will end, how this will end! Noth - ing
non c'e al - cu - na no - vi - tà, co - sì
they will nev-er show their hand. That's the
or ca - pi - sco co - me va! O - ne -
now I see how mat - ters stand. Now at
p

der non può di peg-gio, giu - sti Dei,_ che_
worse than this could hap-pen, no one knows how_
fan tut-te le bel-le, non c'è al - cu - na_
way all wo-men do it, they will nev - er_
stis - si-ma si - gno-ra, or ca - pi - sco_
last_ my eyes are o-pen, now I see_ how_
cresc.

mai sa - rà, giu - sti Dei,_ che_ mai sa - rà, giu - sti
this will end, no one knows how_ this will end, this af -
no - vi - tà, non c'è al - cu - na_ no - vi - tà, non c'è al -
show their hand, they will nev - er_ show their hand, they will
co - me va, or ca - pi - sco_ co - me va, or ca -
mat - ters stand, now I see_ how_ mat - ters stand, now I
p
sfp
cresc.
p

Dei, che mai sa - rà, giu - sti Dei, che mai sa -
- fair is out of hand, no one knows how this will
- cu - na no - vi - tà, non c'è al - cu - na no - vi -
nev - er show their hand, they will nev - er show their
- pi - sco co - me va, or ca - pi - sco co - me
see how mat - ters stand, now I see how mat - ters

rà, giu - sti Dei, che mai sa - rà,
end, this af - fair is out of hand,
tà, co - sì fan tut - te le bel - le, co - sì fan tut - te le bel - le, non c'è al-
hand. That's the way all wo - men do it, that's the way all wo - men do it, they will
va! o - ne - stis - si - ma si - gno - ra, or ca -
stand. Now at last my eyes are o - pen, now I
cresc.
f

che mai sa - rà, che sa - rà, che sa -
is out of hand, out of hand, out of
cu - na no - vi - tà, no - vi - tà, no - vi -
nev - er show their hand, show their hand, show their
pi - sco co - me va, co - me va, co - me
see how mat - ters stand, mat - ters stand, mat - ters
p
calando
rà, che sa - rà!
hand, out of hand.
tà, no - vi - tà!
hand, show their hand.
va, co - me va!
stand, mat - ters stand.
pp

Recitative

Count, Susanna, Cherubino, and Basilio

Susanna
ven-ne? E-gli e-ra me-co, quan-do voi quì giun-ge-ste, e mi chie-de-a d'im-pe-
bi-no? He was with me when we heard you ap-proach-ing. He came to beg me to
gnar la pa-dro-na a inter-ce-der-gli gra-zia. Il vo-stro ar-
plead for my la-dy's gra-cious in-ter-ces-sion. And your ar-
ri-vo in scom-pi-glio lo po-se, ed al-lor in quel lo-co si na-
ri-val com-plete-ly up-set him, so he hid in that chair in des-per-
Count
sco-se. Ma s'io stes-so m'as-si-si, quan-do in ca-me-ra en-
a-tion. But I sat in that arm-chair when I en-tered the
Cherubino (timidly)
Count
tra-i! Ed al-lo-ra di die-tro io mi ce-la-i. E
room. At that time I was hid-ing be-hind it. But when

Cherubino
quan-do io là mi po - si? Al - lor io pian mi vol - si, e quì m'a -
I stepped be-hind it? Then I slipped in - to the seat, un-der this
Count (to Susanna)
sco - si. Oh, cie - lo! dun-que ha sen - ti - to quel - lo ch'io
cov - er. Con - found it! then he has heard the whole of our
Cherubino
ti di - ce - a! Fe - ci per non sen - tir quan - to po -
con - ver - sa - tion! I tried my ver - y best not to
Count
Basilio
Count (pull-
te - a. Oh, per - fi - dia! Fre - na - te - vi, vien gen - te. E
lis - ten. Oh, you ras - cal! Some-one's com-ing— be care - ful! And
ing Cherubino out of the arm-chair)
voi re - sta - te qui, pic - ciol ser - pen - te!
you stand up at once, you lit - tle ser - pent!

No. 8. Giovani liete

Strew in his praises

Chorus

Countrymen and women

(Enter Figaro, carrying a white veil in his hand, and Peasants, dressed in white, who strew flowers from small baskets before the Count.)

f
Il suo gran co - re vi ser-ba in-tat - to,
He has re-spect - ed, no - bly pro-tect - ed
f
Il suo gran co - re vi ser-ba in-tat - to,
He has re-spect - ed, no - bly pro-tect - ed
p
D'un più bel fio - re l'al - mo can-dor,
Maid - en - ly hon - or, vir - tue's re - ward,
p
D'un più bel fio - re l'al - mo can-dor,
Maid - en - ly hon - or, vir - tue's re - ward,
p
cresc.
f
d'un più bel fio - re l'al - mo can -
maid - en - ly hon - or, vir - tue's re -
f
d'un più bel fio - re l'al - mo can -
maid - en - ly hon - or, vir - tue's re -
f

dor. Gio-va-ni lie - te, fio - ri spar-ge-te Da-van-ti il
ward. He is sa - ga - cious, friend - ly and gra-cious in his be -
dor. Gio-va-ni lie - te, fio - ri spar-ge-te Da-van-ti il
ward. He is sa - ga - cious, friend - ly and gra-cious in his be -
no-bi-le no - stro si-gnor, no - stro si -
nev-o-lence, loved and a-dored, loved and a -
no-bi-le no - stro si-gnor, no - stro si -
nev-o-lence, loved and a-dored, loved and a -
gnor, no - stro si-gnor.
dored, our no-ble lord.
gnor, no - stro si-gnor.
dored, our no-ble lord.

Recitative and Chorus

Count, Figaro, Susanna, and Chorus

Count
Figaro
a - ma. Quel drit-to or non v'è più, co-sa si bra-ma? Del-la
cere - ly. That cus-tom has been an - nulled, why do you wor-ry? We
vo-stra sag-gez-za il pri - mo frut-to og - gi no - i co-glie -
are the first ones to reap the fruits of the new de -
rem: le no - stre noz - ze si son già sta - bi -
cree. We have al - read - y set the time for our
li - te, or a voi toc - ca co - stei che un vo - stro do - no il - li -
wed-ding, and call u - pon you to place this sym-bol of vir - tue on the

ba - ta ser-bò, co-prir di que - sto sim - bo - lo d'o - ne - sta, can - di - da
head of my bride, chaste and spot - less, thanks to your no - ble deed, your gen-'rous
Count
ve - sta. (Dia - bo - li-ca a-stu - zia! ma fin-ge - re con-vien.) Son gra-to, a -
ac - tion. (What dev - il - ish cun - ning! but I will play a - long.) I'm tru - ly
mi - ci, ad un sen - so sì o - ne - sto! Ma non mer - to per
grate - ful for your keen un - der - stand - ing; but I mer - it no
que - sto, nè tri - bu - ti, nè lo - di, è un drit-to in-giu - sto ne' miei
cred - it, nei-ther trib - ute nor prais - es for chang-ing laws which were un -
feu - di a - bo - len - do, a na - tu - ra, al do - ver lor drit - ti io
just and im - mor - al. I am bound to up-hold the rights of

All
Susanna
(sarcastically)
Figaro
ren - do. Ev - vi - va! ev - vi - va! ev - vi - va! Che vir - tù! Che giu -
na - ture. Three cheers for our gen - er - ous mas - ter! He is great! He is
Count (to Figaro and Susanna)
sti - zia! A voi pro - met - to com - pier la ce - ri - mo - nia,
no - ble! You have my prom - ise to cel - e - brate this mar - riage.
chie - do sol bre - ve in - du - gio; io vo - glio in fac - cia de' miei più
Give me a lit - tle time, though, I need it, to gath - er my faith - ful
fi - di, e con più ric - ca pom - pa ren - der - vi ap - pien fe - li - ci. (Mar - cel -
sub - jects; then with fit - ting pomp and cir - cum - stance I shall u - nite you. (I will
li - na si tro - vi.) An - da - te, a - mi - ci.
send for Mar - cel - li - na.) Fare - well, till lat - er.

Chorus

(The Peasants strew the rest of the flowers.)
SOPRANO
ALTO
Gio - va - ni lie - te, fio - ri spar -
Strew in his prais - es ros - es and
TENOR
BASS
Gio - va - ni lie - te, fio - ri spar -
Strew in his prais - es ros - es and
ge - te, Da - van - ti il no - bi - le
dai - sies, Let us all hon - or him,
ge - te, Da - van - ti il no - bi - le
dai - sies, Let us all hon - or him,
cresc.
no - stro si - gnor. Il suo gran co - re
mas - ter and lord. He has re - spect - ed,
no - stro si - gnor. Il suo gran co - re
mas - ter and lord. He has re - spect - ed,

vi ser - ba in - tat - to, D'un più bel
nob - ly pro - tect - ed Maid - en - ly
vi ser - ba in - tat - to, D'un più bel
nob - ly pro - tect - ed Maid - en - ly
fio - re l'al - mo can - dor, d'un più bel
hon - or, vir - tue's re - ward, Maid - en - ly
fio - re l'al - mo can - dor, d'un più bel
hon - or, vir - tue's re - ward, Maid - en - ly
cresc.
fio - re l'al - mo can - dor. Gio - va - ni lie - te,
hon - or, vir - tue's re - ward. He is sa - ga - cious,
fio - re l'al - mo can - dor. Gio - va - ni lie - te,
hon - or, vir - tue's re - ward. He is sa - ga - cious,

fio - ri spar - ge - te Da - van - ti il no - bi - le
friendly and gra - cious in his be - nev - o - lence,
fio - ri spar - ge - te Da - van - ti il no - bi - le
friendly and gra - cious in his be - nev - o - lence,
no - stro si - gnor, no - stro si -
loved and a - dored, loved and a -
no - stro si - gnor, no - stro si -
loved and a - dored, loved and a -
(Exeunt Peasants.)
gnor, no - stro si - gnor.
dored, our no - ble lord!
gnor, no - stro si - gnor.
dored, our no - ble lord!

Recitative

Figaro, Susanna, Basilio, Cherubino, and Count

Cherubino (kneeling)
Count
Susanna
mi - ra! Per - do - no, mio si - gnor! Nol me - ri - ta - te. E-gli è an-
wed - ding? For - give me, no - ble lord! You don't de-serve it. He is
Count
Cherubino
co - ra fan - ciul - lo. Men di quel che tu cre - di. È ver, man -
on - ly a child. Don't be - lit - tle his tal - ents. I may be
Count (raising Cherubino from his knees)
ca - i; ma dal mio lab-bro al - fi - ne — Ben, ben, io vi per -
lit - tle, but I hear like a grown - up. E - nough. I will for -
do - no. An - zi fa - rò di più; va - can-te è un po - sto d'uf - fi -
give you. And I will do e - ven more: I need a cap - tain in my
(The Count prepares to
zial nel reg - gi - men-to mi - o! Io scel-go voi, par - ti - te to - sto, ad -
reg - i - ment sta-tioned at Se-ville. The post is yours, de - part at once. Good -

leave; Susanna and Figaro detain him.)
Susanna and Figaro
Count
Cherubino (sighing
di - o! Ah! fin do-ma-ni sol! No, par-ta to-sto. A ub-bi-dir-vi, si -
bye! Please let him stay to-day... No, you have heard me. I'm pre-pared to o -
with great feeling)
Count
gnor, son già dis-po-sto. Via per l'ul-ti-ma vol-ta la Su-san-na ab-brac -
bey your lord-ship's or-der. For the ver-y last time, kiss Su-san-na good -
(Cherubino embraces Susanna, who is still confused.)
Figaro
(Exeunt the Count and Basilio)
cia-te. (In-a-spet-ta-to è il col-po.) Ehi, ca-pi-ta-no, a me pu-re la
bye. (That was a stroke of ge-nius!) Well, mis-ter cap-tain, best of luck on your
(softly, to Cherubino)
(with feigned joy)
ma-no. (Io vuò par-lar-ti pria che tu par-ta.) Ad-di-o,
jour-ney. (De-spite his or-der, stay till to-mor-row.) Good-bye, now,
pic-cio-lo Che-ru-bi-no! Co-me can-gia in un pun-to il tuo de-sti-no!
dear lit-tle Che-ru-bi-no! What a glo-ri-ous fu-ture lies be-fore you!

No. 9. Non più andrai
From now on
Aria
Figaro

Non più a - vrai que-sti bei pen-nac-chi - ni, quel cap -
You had bet-ter for-get all your fin - 'ry, feath-ered
p
f
p
pel - lo leg - gie - ro e ga - lan - te, quel - la chio - ma, quell' a - ria bril -
caps which you wore to per - fec - tion; pow-dered ring - lets and cream - like com -
tr
tr
lan - te, quel ver - mi - glio don - ne - sco co - lor, quel ver -
plex - ion in the ar - my will soon dis - ap - pear, in the
tr
sf
tr
cresc.
mi - glio don - ne - sco co - lor! Non più a -
ar - my will soon dis - ap - pear! You had
f
p

vrai quei pen-nac-chi-ni, quel cap-
best for-get your fin-'ry, feath-ered
pel-lo, quel-la chio-ma, quell' a-ria bril-lan-te! Non più an-
caps, pow-dered ring-lets, and cream-like com-plex-ion. From now
cresc.
f
p
drai, far-fal-lo-ne a-mo-ro-so, not-te e gior-no d'in-tor-no gion, my ad-ven-tur-ous lov-er, no ro-man-tic phi-lan-d'ring ex-
ran-do, del-le bel-le tur-ban-do il ri-po-so, Nar-ci-
cur-sions. Such di-ver-sions are done with and o-ver, Che-ru-
ten.
ten.

set - to, A - don - ci - no d'a - mor, del - le bel - le tur - ban - do il ri -
bi - no, my young cav - a - lier, such di - ver - sions are done with and
ten. ten.
po - so, Nar - ci - set - to, A - don - ci - no d'a - mor.
o - ver, Che - ru - bi - no, my young cav - a - lier.
mf p f
Fra guer - rie - ri, pof - far Bac - co! gran mus - tac - chi, stret - to
Off with sol - diers coarse - ly swear - ing, long mus - tach - es proud - ly
sac - co, schiop - po in spal - la, scia - bla al fian - co, col - lo drit - to, mu - so
wear - ing! With a ri - fle and a sa - ber, in the ar - my you will

fran - co, un gran ca - sco, o un gran tur - ban - te, mol-to o -
la - bor, trum-pets clash - ing and hel-mets flash - ing, lots of
nor, po-co con-tan - te, po - co con - tan - te, po - co con - tan - te. Ed in
fame, but not much mon - ey, but not much mon - ey, but not much mon - ey, and in -
p
ve - ce del fan - dan - go u - na
stead of min - u - et - ting, through the
p
cresc.
mar - cia per il fan - go. Per mon - ta - gne, per val -
mud you'll stag - ger sweat - ing. Up the ston - y moun - tains
f
p

lo - ni,
wheez - ing,
con le ne - vi, e i sol - lio - ni, al con - cer - to di trom -
some - times broil - ing, some - times freez - ing, to the tune of trum - pets
bo - ni, di bom - bar - de, di can - no - ni, che le pal - le in tut - ti i
wail - ing, while the can - non - balls are hail - ing and the ri - fle bul - lets
tuo - ni, all' o - rec - chio fan fi - schiar.
sail - ing, whis - tling by your pret - ty ear.
Non più a -
You had
vrai quei pen - nac - chi - ni, non più a -
best for - get your fin - 'ry which you
f
p
f

vrai quel cap - pel - lo, non più a -
wore to per - fec - tion, and for -
p
f
vrai quel - la chio - ma, non più a -
get feath-ered caps, pow-dered
p
cresc.
vrai quell' a - ria bril - lan - te! Non più an-drai, far-fal-lo - ne a-mo-
curls and cream - like com - plex - ion. From now on, my ad-ven - tur - ous
f
p
ro - so, not-te e gior - no d'in-tor - no gi - ran - do, del - le
lov - er, no ro-man - tic, phi-lan - d'ring ex-cur - sions. Such di -

bel - le tur-ban-do il ri - po - so, Nar - ci - set - to, A - don - ci - no d'a -
ver - sions are done with and o - ver, Che - ru - bi - no, my young cav - a -
ten. ten.
mf p
mor, del - le bel - le tur-ban-do il ri - po - so, Nar - ci -
lier. Such di - ver - sions are done with and o - ver, Che - ru -
ten.
mf p
set - to, A-don-ci - no d'a - mor. Che - ru - bi-no, al - la vit -
bi - no, my young cav - a - lier. Che - ru - bi - no, on to
to - ria, al - la glo-ria mi - li - tar, Che - ru -
glo - ry, on to vic - t'ry and to fame, Che - ru -

bi-no, al-la vit-to-ria, al-la glo-ria mi-li-tar, al-la
bi-no, on to glo-ry, on to glo-ry and to fame, on to
(Exeunt in military style.)
glo-ria mi-li-tar, al-la glo-ria mi-li-tar!
glo-ry and to fame, on to glo-ry and to fame.

End of Act I

Act II

(Scene: *A luxurious room, with an alcove and three doors.*)

No. 10. Porgi, amor, qualche ristoro

Pour, O love, sweet consolation

Cavatina

Countess

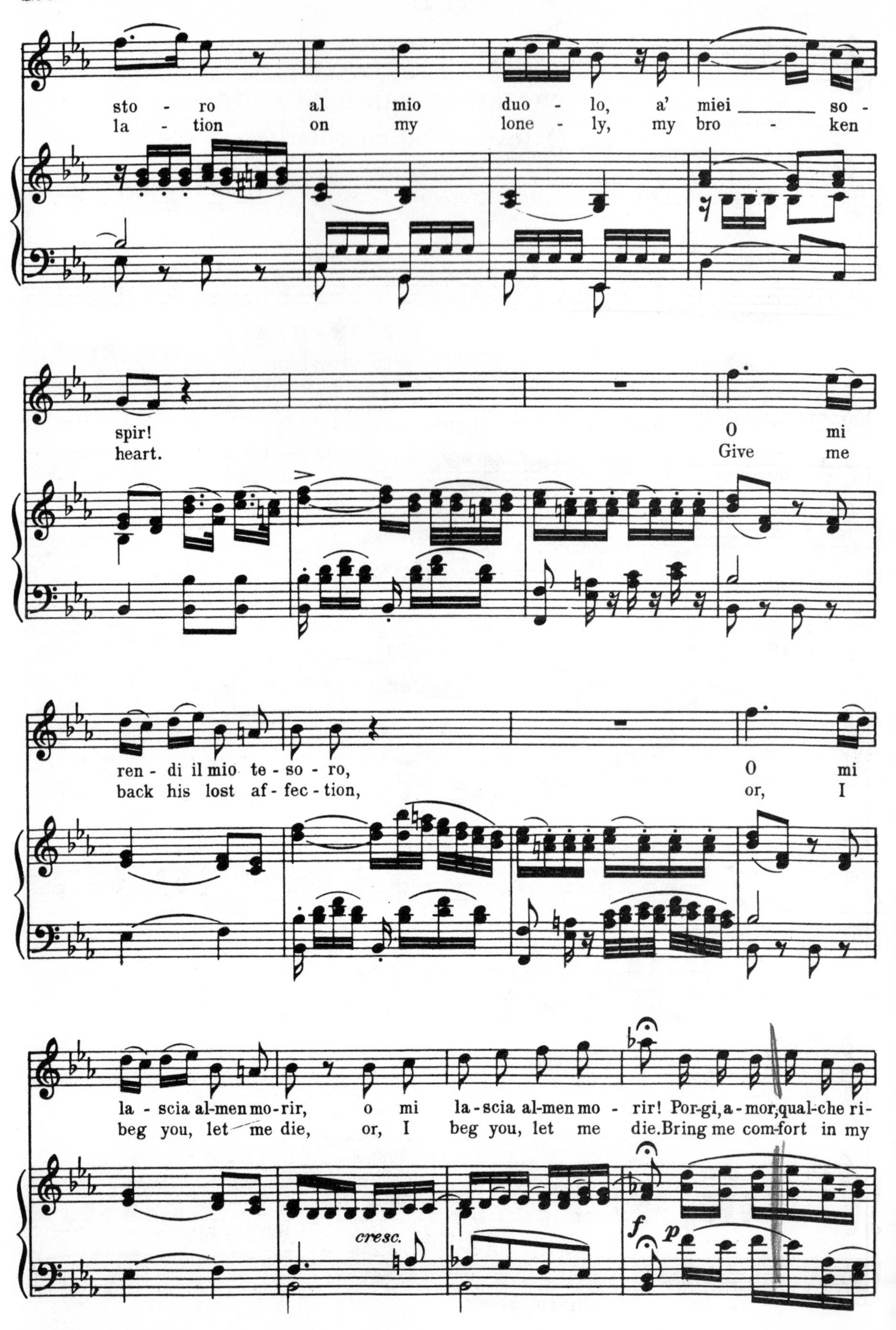
sto - ro al mio duo - lo, a' miei so -
la - tion on my lone - ly, my bro - ken
spir! O mi
heart. Give me
ren - di il mio te - so - ro, O mi
back his lost af - fec - tion, or, I
la - scia al-men mo-rir, o mi la - scia al-men mo - rir! Por-gi, a - mor, qual-che ri -
beg you, let me die, or, I beg you, let me die. Bring me com-fort in my
cresc.
f
p

sto - ro al mio duo - lo, a' miei so - spir! O mi ren - di il mio te -
suf - f'ring, hear my bro - ken - heart - ed sigh! Give me back my lord and
so - ro, o mi la - - scia al - men mo - rir, al -
hus - band, or, I beg you, let me die, or
men mo - rir, o mi ren - di il mio te - so - ro, o mi
let me die, give me back my lord and hus - band, or, I
la - scia al - men mo - rir!
beg you, let me die!
p

Recitative

Countess, Susanna, and Figaro

Countess
poi è ge-lo-so di voi? Co-me lo so-no i mo-der-ni ma-ri-ti, per si-
then, that he's jeal-ous of you? It is the same way with all mod-ern hus-bands, by
ste-ma in-fe-de-li, per ge-nio ca-pric-cio-si, e per or-go-glio poi tut-ti ge-
na-ture un-faith-ful, by char-ac-ter ca-pri-cious, and con-ceit-ed e-nough to be
lo-si. Ma se Fi-ga-ro t'a-ma, ei sol po-tri-a...
jeal-ous. But if Fi-ga-ro loves you, he might be a-ble...
[Presto]
Figaro (Enters singing.)
La la la la la la la la la la la la la la la la la la la
p
f

Susanna
Figaro (with casual gaiety)
la. Ec - co - lo, vie - ni, a - mi - co, ma - da - ma im - pa - zien - te. A voi non
There he is! Come, my dar - ling, my la - dy is wait - ing. No need to
toc - ca sta - re in pe - na per que - sto. Al - fin di che si
wor - ry, there's no rea - son what - ev - er. The mat - ter's ver - y
trat - ta? Al si - gnor Con - te pia - ce la spo - sa mi - a;
sim - ple: my no - ble lord takes a fan - cy to my Su - san - na,
in - di se - cre - ta - men - te ri - cu - pe - rar vor - ri - a il di -
so he de - cides in se - cret that he'll re - store a cus - tom he has
rit - to feu - da - le; pos - si - bi - le è la co - sa e na - tu -
late - ly a - bol - ished; the thing is ver - y pos - si - ble and ver - y

Countess
Susanna
Figaro
ra - le. Pos - si - bil? Na - tu - ral? Na - tu - ra -
nat - u - ral. Ver - y pos - si - ble? Ver - y nat - u - ral? It is most
lis - si - ma, e se Su - san - na vuol, pos - si - bi -
nat - u - ral, and, if Su - san - na wants it, is most
Susanna
Figaro
lis - si - ma. Fi - ni - sci - la u - na vol - ta. Ho già fi - ni - to,
pos - si - ble. When will you ev - er fin - ish? I have al - read - y.
quin - di pre - se il par - ti - to, di sce - glier me cor - rie - ro, e la Su -
That is why he de - cid - ed he needs me as his cour - ier and that Su -
san - na con - si - glie - ra se - gre - ta d'am - ba - scia - ta; e perch' el - la o - sti -
san - na should be - come his am - bas - sa - dress in se - cret; and be - cause she has

na - ta o - gnor ri - fiu - ta il di - plo - ma d'o - nor, ch'ei le de - sti - na, mi -
stub-born - ly re - fused to ac-cept the as - sign - ment, he's of - fend - ed and
nac - cia di pro - teg - ger Mar - cel - li - na; que - sto è tut - to l'af -
threat-ens to take sides with Mar - cel - li - na; that's the gist of the
Susanna
fa - re. Ed hai co - rag - gio di trat - tar scher - zan - do un ne -
sto - ry. How can you treat such a ser - ious busi - ness as a
Figaro
go - zio si se - rio? Non vi ba - sta, che scher - zan - do io ci
mat - ter of jok - ing? Aren't you hap - py that I don't take it
pen - si? Ec - co il pro - get - to: per Ba - si - lio un bi - gliet - to io gli
ser - ious - ly? Here is my proj - ect: through Ba - si - lio I'll send a lit - tle

(to the
fo ca-pi-tar, che l'av-ver-ti-sca di cer-to ap-pun-ta-men-to, che per
note to the Count to in-form him a-bout an ap-point-ment that the
Countess)
l'o-ra del bal-lo a un a-man-te voi de-ste.
Count-ess sup-pos-ed-ly made with a lov-er.
Countess
O ciel!
Good Lord!
che sen-to! ad un uom si ge-lo-so-
How risk-y! With a hus-band so jeal-ous!
Figaro
An-co-ra me-glio, co-
So much the bet-ter. Be-
si po-trem più pre-sto im-ba-raz-zar-lo, con-fon-der-lo, im-bro-gliar-lo,
cause we can more read-i-ly at-tack him, and baf-fle him, dis-con-cert him,
ro-ve-sciar-gli i pro-get-ti, em-pier-lo di so-spet-ti, e por-gli in
get him whol-ly be-wil-dered, in-flame him with sus-pi-cion, and make him

te - sta, che la mo-der-na fe - sta ch'ei di fa-re a me ten-ta, al-tri a lui
grasp that what he does to oth - ers they will do un-to him, and e - ven with
fac - cia, on - de quà per - da il tem-po, i - vi la trac-cia, co -
in - t'rest! While he is los - ing time as well as his bear-ings, our
sì qua-si ex ab - rup - to, e sen-za ch'ab-bia fat - to per fra-sto - nar-ci al-cun di
wed-ding hour will come be-fore he ev - er finds an op - por - tu - ni - ty to
(indicating the Countess)
se-gno vien l'o-ra del-le noz-ze, in fac-cia a lei non fia, ch'o-si d'op-por-si ai vo - ti
hin-der us from get-ting mar-ried, or has a chance to make an-y ef-fec-tive op-po -
Susanna
Figaro
mie - i. È ver, ma in di lui ve-ce s'op-por-rà Mar-cel-li - na. A -
si - tion. That's true, but in his stead Mar-cel-li-na will op-pose us. I

spet - ta, al Con - te fa - rai su - bi - to dir, che ver - so
know it, so there - fore: you give the Count a hint that late this
se - ra at - ten - da - ti in giar - di - no; il pic - ciol Che - ru -
eve - ning you'll meet him in the gar - den, and lit - tle Che - ru -
bi - no, per mio con - si - glio non an - cor par - ti - to, da fem - mi - na ve -
bi - no (on my ad - vice he has not yet de - part - ed), dressed up as a
sti - to, fa - re - mo che in sua ve - ce i - vi sen va - da; que - sta è
wo - man, will keep the ren - dez - vous in place of Su - san - na. That's the
l'u - ni - ca stra - da, on - de Mon - sù sor - pre - so da Ma - da - ma, sia co -
on - ly so - lu - tion where - by his lordship, sur - prised by my la - dy, can be

Countess
Susanna
stret-to a far poi quel che si bra-ma. Che ti par? Non c'è mal.
forced to ac-cede to all her dic-tates. How is that? Good e-nough.
Countess
Susanna
Figaro
Nel no-stro ca-so... Quand' e-gli è per-sua-so... E do-ve è il tem-po? I-to è il
All things con-sid-ered... If he thinks it will work... but is there time left? The
Con-te al-la cac-cia, e per qualch' o-ra non sa-rà di ri-
Count has gone hunt-ing and won't come back for at least sev-'ral
(about to go)
tor-no; io va-do, e to-sto Che-ru-bi-no vi man-do, la-scio a
hours. I'll go now and send you Che-ru-bi-no im-med-iate-ly. You have
Countess
Figaro
voi la cu-ra di ve-stir-lo. E po-i? E po-i?
am-ple time to get him read-y. And then? And then?

Figaro
Allegretto
Se vuol bal - la - re, si - gnor Con - ti - no, il chi - tar - ri - no
Should my dear mas - ter want some di - ver - sion, I'll play the mu - sic
(Exit Figaro.)
le suo - ne - rò, sì, le suo - ne - rò, sì, le suo - ne - rò.
on my gui - tar, yes, I'll play the mu - sic on my gui - tar!
Recitative
Countess, Susanna, and Cherubino
Countess
Quan - to duol - mi, Su - san - na, che que - sto gio - vi -
How it grieves me, Su - san - na, to think that Che - ru -
net - to ab - bia del Con - te le stra - va - gan - ze u - di - to! ah! tu non sa - i
bi - no heard all the non - sense my way - ward hus - band told you. Ah, you don't know yet . . .
ma per qual cau - sa ma - i da me stes - sa ei non ven - ne? Dov' è la can - zo -
but for what earth - ly rea - son did - n't he see me in per - son? Where did you put his

Susanna
net-ta? Ec-co-la, ap-pun-to fac-ciam che ce la can-ti. Zit-to, vien
love-song? Here it is; as soon as he comes we'll have him sing it. Lis-ten, who
(Enter Cherubino.)
Cherubino
gen-te, è des-so: a-van-ti, a-van-ti, si-gnor uf-fi-zi-a-le! Ah, non chia-
is it? Our he-ro! Come in, come in, most worth-y ma-jor gen-'ral. Please do not
mar-mi con no-me sì fa-ta-le! ei mi ram-men-ta, che ab-
call me by such a fa-tal ti-tle, for it re-minds me that
Susanna
ban-do-nar degg'-i-o co-ma-re tan-to buo-na! E tan-to
soon I must leave her, my dear-est, kind-est la-dy... Who is so
Cherubino (sighing)
Susanna (mocking him)
bel-la. Ah sì, cer-to! Ah sì, cer-to! i-po-cri-
pret-ty! So sweet, so love-ly. So sweet, so love-ly! You lit-tle

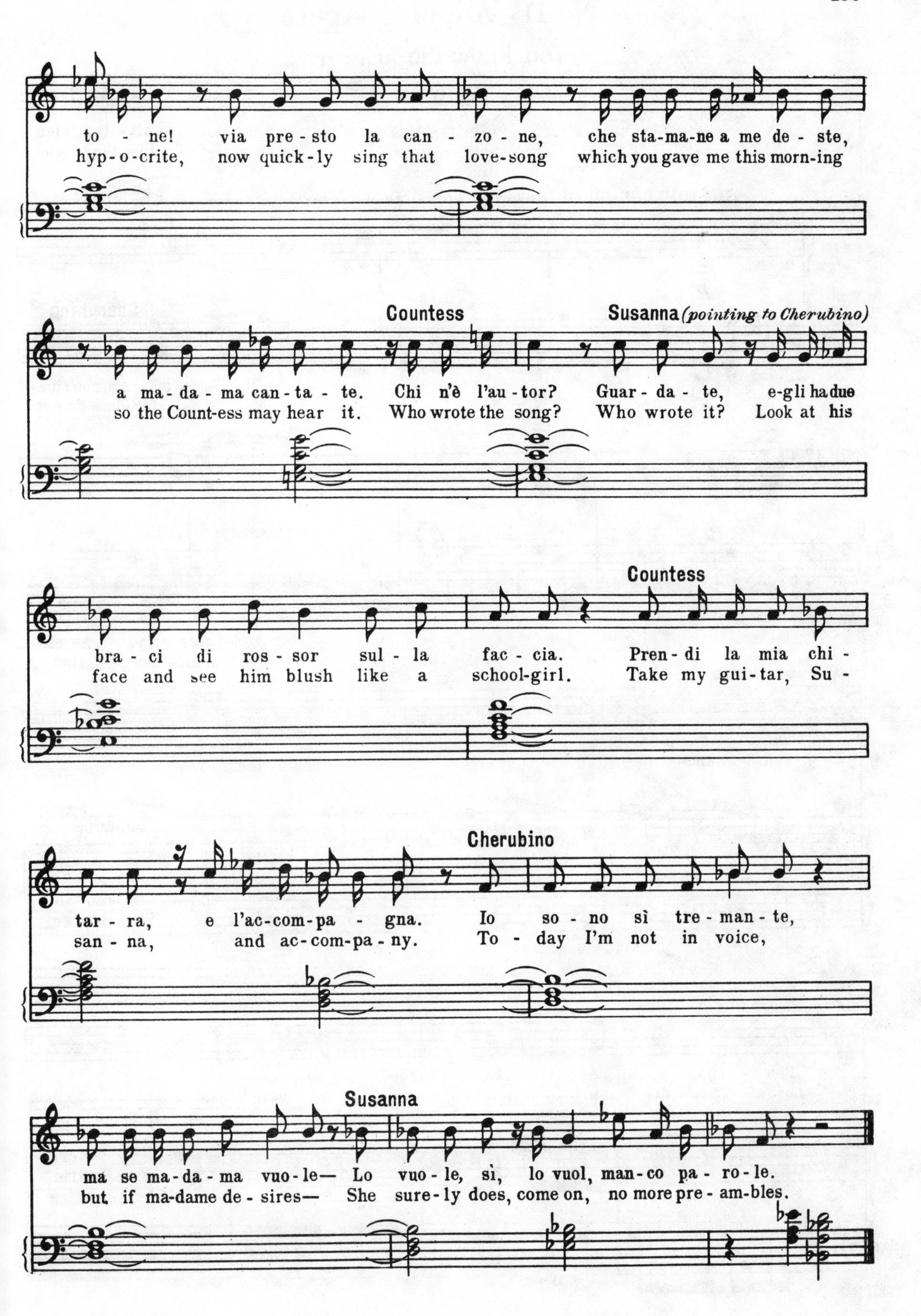
to - ne! via pre - sto la can - zo - ne, che sta-ma-ne a me de - ste,
hyp-o-crite, now quick-ly sing that love-song which you gave me this morn-ing
Countess
Susanna (pointing to Cherubino)
a ma-da - ma can-ta - te. Chi n'è l'au-tor? Guar-da - te, e-gli ha due
so the Count-ess may hear it. Who wrote the song? Who wrote it? Look at his
Countess
bra - ci di ros - sor sul - la fac - cia. Pren - di la mia chi -
face and see him blush like a school-girl. Take my gui - tar, Su -
Cherubino
tar - ra, e l'ac-com-pa - gna. Io so - no sì tre - man - te,
san - na, and ac-com-pa - ny. To - day I'm not in voice,
Susanna
ma se ma-da - ma vuo - le— Lo vuo - le, sì, lo vuol, man-co pa - ro - le.
but if ma-dame de - sires— She sure - ly does, come on, no more pre - am - bles.

No.11. Voi, che sapete

You know the answer

Arietta

Cherubino

Don - ne, ve - de - te, s'io l'ho nel cor.
La - dies, I beg you, share it with me.
Quel - lo ch'io pro - vo, vi - ri - di - rò,
This new sen - sa - tion I un - der - go,
È per me nuo - vo ca - pir nol so.
It is so dif - f'rent from all I know.
Sen - to un af - fet - to pien di de - sir,
Filled with ex - cite - ment, walk - ing on air,

Ch'o - ra è di - let - to, ch'o - ra è mar - tir.
First I am hap - py, soon I de - spair.
Ge - lo, e poi sen - to l'al - ma av-vam - par,
Now I am chil - ly, next time a - flame,
E in un mo - men - to tor - no a ge - lar.
Not for a mo - ment am I the same.
Ri - cer - co un be - ne fuo - ri di me,
I am pur - su - ing some sun - ny ray,

Non so chi il tie - ne, non so cos' è. So-spi-ro e
But it e - ludes me, try as I may. I can't stop
ge-mo sen-za vo-ler, Pal-pi-to e tre-mo sen-za sa-
sigh-ing, hard as I try, And then I trem-ble, not know-ing
per. Non tro-vo pa-ce not-te, nè dì, Ma pur mi pia - ce
why. From this di - lem-ma I find no peace, And yet I want it
lan - guir co-sì. Voi, che sa-pe - te
nev - er to cease. You know the an - swer,
fp
mfp

64
che co-saè a-mor, Don - ne, ve - de - te,
you hold the_ key, Love's ten-der se - cret,
3
68
s'io l'ho nel cor, Don - ne, ve - de - te,_
share it with me, La - dies, I beg_ you,_
3
72
s'io l'ho nel cor, Don - ne, ve - de - te,_
share it with me, La - dies, I beg_ you,_
76
s'io l'ho_ nel_ cor.
share it_ with_ me.
tr
tr

Recitative

Countess, Susanna, and Cherubino

(Takes off his cloak.)
Countess
Susanna
gua - le sta - tu - ra— giù quel man - to. Che fa - i? Nien - te pa - u - ra.
just a-bout my size. Take your coat off. Be care - ful! No need to wor - ry.
Countess
Susanna
E se qual - cu - no en - tras - se? En - tri, che mal fac -
If some - bod - y should en - ter? Let him, what harm are we
(locking the door)
cia - mo? La por - ta chiu - de - rò, ma co - me
do - ing? But I must lock the door. What shall we
Countess
poi ac-con-ciar-gli i ca-pel - li? U - na mia cuf - fia pren - di nel ga - bi - net - to,
do so his hair will not show? Get him a bon-net out of my ward-robe dress-er,
(Susanna goes into the small room to get a bonnet. Cherubino approaches the Countess and
Cherubino
Countess
pre - sto! Che car - ta è quel - la? La pa - ten - te. Che sol -
hur - ry! What have you got there? My com-mis - sion. They

shows her the commission, which he carries in his pocket. She takes it, opens it, and notices that
Cherubino
Countess
le - ci - ta gen - te! L'eb - bi or or da Ba - si - lio. Dal - la
did - n't waste a mo - ment. I got it from Ba - si - lio. In their
the seal is missing.)
(Returns the commission to him.)
Susanna
(returning
fret - ta, ob - bli - a - to han - no il si - gil - lo. Il si -
hur - ry they e - ven for - got the seal. The
with a cap in her hand)
Countess
Susanna
gil - lo di che? Del - la pa - ten - te. Co - spet - to! che pre -
seal on what? On his com - mis - sion. How could they be so
Countess
mu - ra! Ec - co la cuf - fia. Spic - cia - ti: va
care - less? Here is the bon - net. There you are. That's
be - ne: mi - se - ra - bi - li noi, se il Con - te vie - ne!
per - fect! How dis - as - trous for us if the Count came home now!

No.12. Venite, inginocchiatevi

Come here and kneel in front of me

Aria

Susanna

(While Susanna is
bra - vo, và ben co - sì!
Bra - vo, that's ver - y nice.
dressing his hair, Cherubino regards the Countess tenderly.)
La fac-cia o - ra vol - ge - te-mi,
Now turn your face the oth - er way,
(Continues to dress his hair;
o - là! que-gli oc-chi a me, o - la! que-gli oc-chi a
and look me in the eye! Hold still and let me
she places the bonnet on him.)
me! Drit - tis - si-mo, drit - tis - si-mo, guar - da - te - mi, guar -
try. Look straight at me, not ev-'ry-where, the Count-ess is not
cresc.

da-te-mi!
sit-ting there,
Ma-da-ma quì non è.
so wait till by and by.
f
p
La fac-cia o-ra vol-ge-te-mi,
If you would keep your mind on this
o-là! que-gli oc-chi a me! Drit-
we'd get it o-ver soon. The
tis-si-mo, guar-da-te-mi!
more you play, the more de-lay,
Ma-da-ma, ma-da-ma, quì non
at this rate we'll take all af-ter-
cresc.
f
p
è, ma-da-ma quì non è.
noon, we'll take all af-ter-noon.
Re-sta-te
Can't you be
cresc.
f
p

fer - mo, or via gi - ra - te - vi, guar -
qui - et? Don't be so fid - get - y! Be -
da - te - mi! Bra - vo!
have your - self! That's it.
Più al - to quel col - let - to, quel
The neck - line should be high - er, the
ci - glio un po' più bas - so, le ma - ni sot - to il
skirt a lit - tle low - er, the glance a tri - fle

pet - to, ve - dre - mo po - scia il pas - so, quan - do sa - re - te in
shy - er, the mo - tions slight - ly slow - er. Now you must walk a -
piè, ve - dre - mo po - scia il pas - so, quan - do sa - re - te in
round. We'll give you some sug - ges - tions while you are pas - sing
mfp
piè.
by.
pp
(aside to the Countess)
Mi - ra - te il bric - con -
Just see our pri - ma
cel - lo, mi - ra - te quan - to è bel - lo, che fur - ba guar - da -
don - na! He plays his part with hon - or. The clev - er lit - tle

tu - ra, che vez - zo, che fi - gu - ra! mi - ra - te il bric - con -
sham - mer is full of charm and glam - our. No pow - der or cos -
cel - lo, mi - ra - te quan - to è bel - lo, che fur - ba guar - da -
met - ic would bet - ter his com - plex - ion, his glance is so po -
tu - ra, che vez - zo, che fi - gu - ra! Se l'a - ma - no le
et - ic, his fig - ure is per - fec - tion! If wo - men fall in
cresc.
f p
fem - mi - ne, han cer - to il lor per - chè, se l'a - ma - no, han
love with him, they know the rea - son why, oh, cer - tain - ly, they

cer-to il lor per-chè, han cer-to, cer-to, cer-to il lor per-
know the rea-son why. Yes, yes, I see it clear-ly, the rea-son
sfp
tr
chè,_ han cer-to, cer-to, cer-to il lor per-
why,_ yes, yes, I see it clear-ly, the rea-son
sfp
tr
3
chè, han cer-to, cer-to il lor per-chè, han cer-to, cer-to il lor per-
why. I clear-ly see_ the rea-son why, I clear-ly see_ the rea-son
chè, il lor per-chè, il lor per-chè?
why, the rea-son why, the rea-son why.

Recitative

Countess, Susanna, Cherubino, and Count

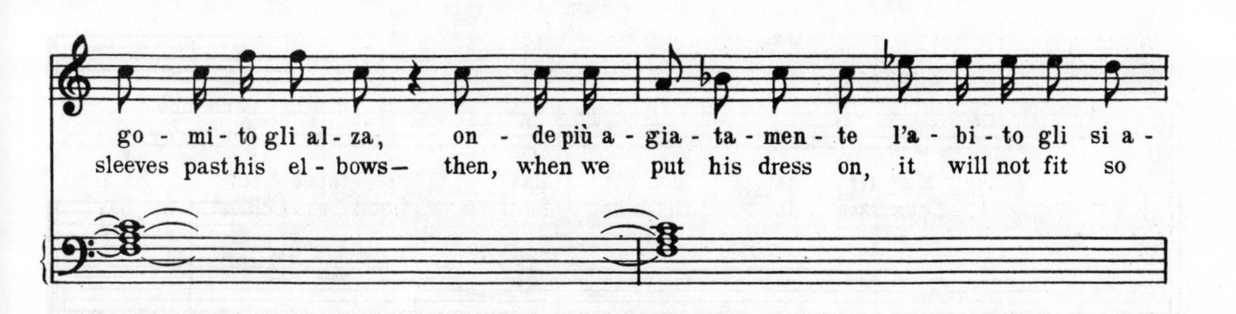

Susanna
(doing so)
Countess
(Discovers a
dat - ti. Ec - co! Più in - die - tro, co - sì. Che na-stro è
tight - ly. This way. Up far - ther, like this. What is that
ribbon wrapped about his arm.)
Susanna
Countess
Cherubino
quel - lo? È quel ch'es-so in - vo - lom - mi. E que-sto san - gue? Quel
rib - bon? The one he stole this morn-ing. Why is it blood-stained? Oh,
san - gue... io non so co - me, po - co pria sdruc-cio - lan - do... in un
real - ly, I can't im - ag - ine; just be - fore, when I stum-bled on the
sas - so... la pel - le io mi sgraf - fia - i... e la pia - ga col na-stro io mi fa -
grav - el, I guess I scraped my el - bow, and I ban-daged the wound with this
Susanna
scia - i? Mo - stra - te: non è mal; co - spet - to! ha il
rib - bon. Let's see it, that's not bad! Good gra - cious! His

Countess
brac-cio più can-di-do del mi-o! qual-che ra-gaz-za... E se-gui a far la
arm is much whit-er than my own, just like a wo-man's! You still keep up this
paz-za? Va nel mio ga-bi-net-to, e pren-di un po-co d'in-gle-se taf-fe-
non-sense? Go and look in my clos-et, and get a piece of ad-he-sive plas-ter,
(Susanna dashes off; the Countess contemplates her ribbon; Cherubino, kneeling,
tà, ch'è sul-lo scri-gno. In quan-to al na-stro... in ver... per il co-
quick, it's in the dres-ser. As for that rib-bon, you know, I like the
observes her attentively.)
Susanna (Gives the plaster and the scissors to the Countess.)
lo-re mi spia-cea di pri-var-me-ne. Te-ne-te, e da le-gar-gli il
col-or, I would hate to part with it. I found it, but don't we need a
Countess
Cherubino
brac-cio? Un al-tro na-stro pren-di in-siem col mio ve-sti-to. Ah,
band-age? An-oth-er rib-bon, bring it a-long when you come back. Ah,

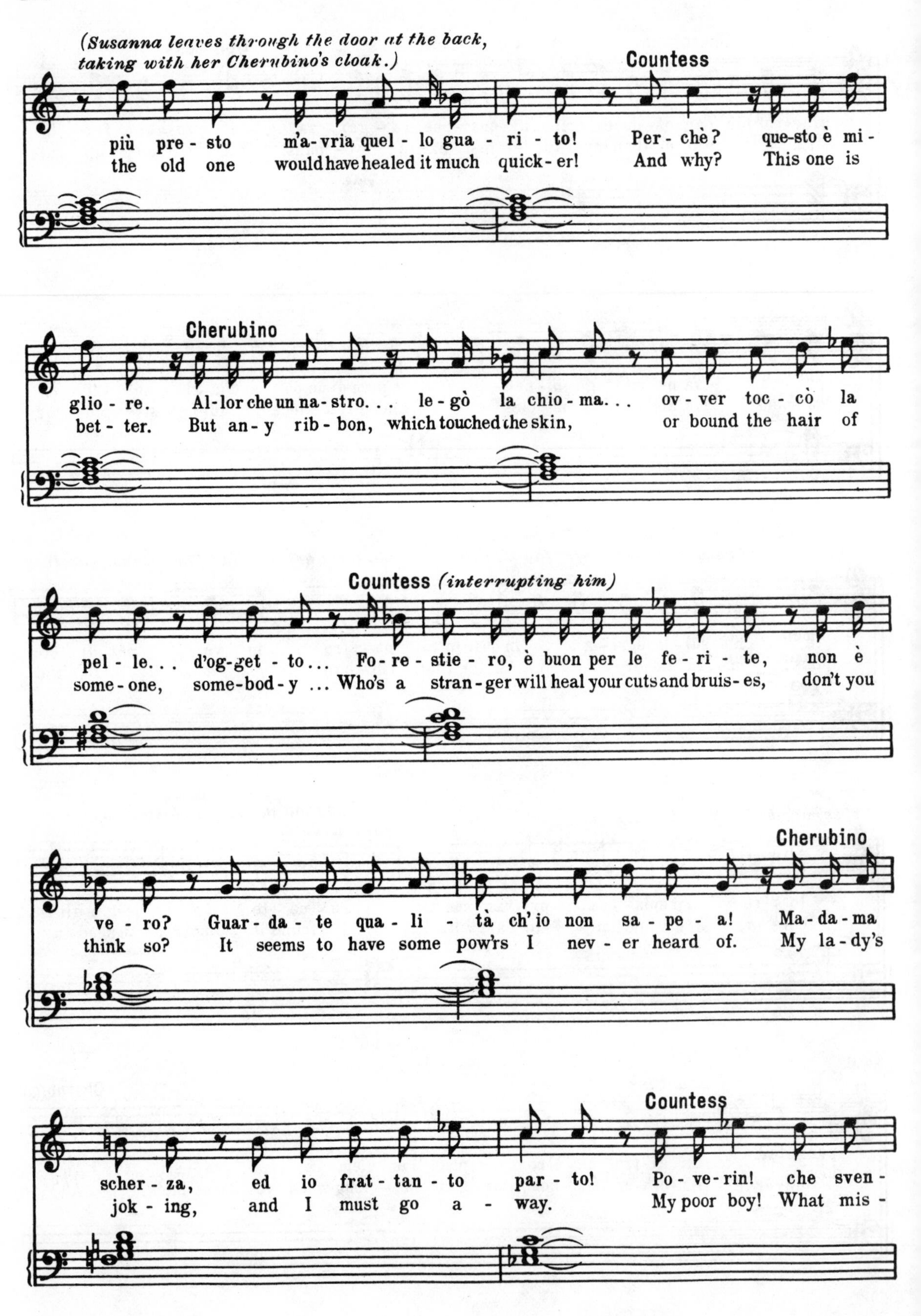
(Susanna leaves through the door at the back, taking with her Cherubino's cloak.)
Countess
più pre - sto m'a-vria quel - lo gua - ri - to! Per - chè? que-sto è mi -
the old one would have healed it much quick - er! And why? This one is
Cherubino
glio - re. Al - lor che un na - stro. . . le - gò la chio - ma. . . ov - ver toc - cò la
bet - ter. But an - y rib - bon, which touched the skin, or bound the hair of
Countess (interrupting him)
pel - le. . . d'og - get - to. . . Fo - re - stie - ro, è buon per le fe - ri - te, non è
some - one, some - bod - y . . . Who's a stran - ger will heal your cuts and bruis - es, don't you
Cherubino
ve - ro? Guar - da - te qua - li - tà ch'io non sa - pe - a! Ma - da - ma
think so? It seems to have some pow'rs I nev - er heard of. My la - dy's
Countess
scher - za, ed io frat - tan - to par - to! Po - ve - rin! che sven -
jok - ing, and I must go a - way. My poor boy! What mis -

Cherubino
Countess (much moved)
Cherubino
tu - ra! Oh me in - fe - li - ce! Or pian - ge... Oh ciel! per -
for - tune! How I am suf - f'ring! You're cry - ing! O Lord, why
chè mo - rir non li - ce! For - se vi - ci - no all' ul - ti - mo mo -
don't you let me die now? Close to my death, I might get up the
Countess (drying his
men - to... que - sta boc - ca o - se - ri - a! Sia - te sag - gio,
cour - age to con - fess how I real - ly... Che - ru - bi - no,
eyes with her handkerchief)
(A knock at the door is heard)
cos' è que - sta fol - li - a? Chi pic - chia al - la mia
you are a lit - tle ba - by! Who's knock - ing at my
Count (outside)
Countess
por - ta? Per - chè chiu - sa? Il mio spo - so! oh De - i! son
door? Why locked in? It's my hus - band! Good Heav - ens! I'm

mor - ta. Voi quì, sen-za man - tel - lo! in que-sto sta - to. . .
ru - ined... with you here with-out your jack - et. . . in this con-di - tion. . .
un ri - ce - vu - to fo - glio, la sua gran ge - lo - si - a. . .
He has re-ceived a let - ter . . . he's so ter - ri - bly jeal - ous!
Count
(more loudly)
Countess (confused)
Count
Co-sa in-du - gia - te? Son so - la. . . ah sì son so - la. E a chi par -
Why this de - lay? I'm a-lone, yes, yes, I'm com-ing. . . To whom were you
Countess
Cherubino
la - te? A vo - i. . . cer - to, a voi stes - so. Do-po
speak-ing? To you. . . sure - ly to you on - ly. Af-ter
quel ch'è suc - ces - so, il suo fu - ro - re. . . non tro-vo al-tro con -
all that has hap-pened, his aw-ful tem-per, I can-not let him

(Runs into the small room and shuts the door.)
Countess
(Takes the key and runs to admit the Count.)
si - glio. Ah! mi di - fen - da il cie - lo in tal pe - ri - glio!
find me. May God a - bove pro - tect me in this dan - ger!
Count
(Enters, in hunting costume.)
Che no - vi - tà! non fu mai vo-stra u-san - za di rin-chiu - der-vi in stan - za.
This is some-thing new! It was nev - er your cus - tom to lock your-self in!
Countess
È ver; ma i - o. . . io sta - va quì met - ten - do. . .
That's true, but this time. . . I on - ly was ar - rang - ing. . .
Count
Via met - ten - do. . .
Ar - rang - ing. . .
Countess
Cer - te ro - be, e - ra me - co la Su - san - na, che in sua ca - me - ra è an - da - ta.
Some of my dress - es, and Su - san - na was with me; she has gone in - to her own room. . .
Count
Ad o - gni mo - do voi non sie - te tran - quil - la. Guar - da - te que - sto
At an - y rate, it seems that some - thing up - set you. Can you ex - plain this

Countess [aside]
(Cherubino, in the small room, noisily knocks over a small table and chair.)
Count
fo-glio. Nu-mi! è il fo-glio che Fi-ga-ro gli scris-se. Cos' è co-de-sto
let-ter? Heav-ens! The let-ter that Fi-ga-ro has writ-ten! What was that aw-ful
Countess
stre-pi-to? In ga-bi-net-to qual-che co-sa è ca-du-ta. Io non in-te-si
noise in there? A piece of fur-ni-ture fell down in your bou-doir. Strange, I did not
Count
Countess
Count
nien-te. Con-vien che ab-bia-te i gran pen-sie-ri in men-te. Di che? Là v'è qual-
hear it. In that e-vent, you must be hard of hear-ing. Who, I? Some-bod-y's
Countess
Count
cu-no. Chi vo-le-te che si-a? Lo chie-do a vo-i, io ven-go in que-sto
in there! Who could pos-si-bly be there? I'm ask-ing you that, I on-ly just came
Countess
Count
pun-to. Ah! sì... Su-san-na... ap-pun-to... Che pas-
in here. Of course, Su-san-na. How could I... Just be-

Countess
sò, mi di - ce - ste, al - la sua stan - za. Al - la sua stan - za, o
fore, you were say - ing she went to her room. May-be to her room, or
Count
quì, non vi - di be - ne. Su - san - na, e d'on - de vie - ne che sie - te sì tur-
that one, I was not watch-ing. Then tell me, how does it hap-pen that you are so em-
Countess (with a forced laugh)
Count
ba - ta? Per la mia ca-me-riè - ra? Io non so nul - la; ma tur - ba - ta senz'
bar-rassed? For what pos - si-ble rea - son? I can't ex-plain it, but you do seem em-
Countess
al - tro. Ah que - sta ser - va più che non tur - ba me, tur - ba voi stes - so.
bar-rassed. Is it not you, rath - er, who should be em - bar-rassed — a - bout Su - san - na?
Count
È ve - ro, è ve - ro, e lo ve - dre - te a - des - so.
That's not the is - sue! If it's Su - san - na, I must see her.
[attacca subito]

No. 13. Susanna, or via sortite!

Susanna, what's the matter?

Terzetto

Count, Countess, and Susanna

(Susanna enters through the door she used on leaving, and halts, on seeing the Count at the door of the small room.)

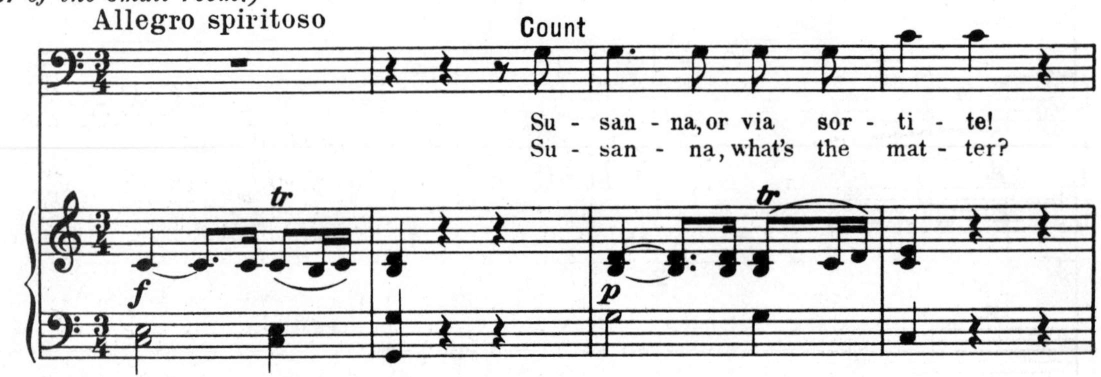

dò? il paggio dove andò?
here? The page no longer here?
Count
può, sortire ella non può. E chi vietarlo or
pear, right now she can't appear! What reason can pre-
cresc.
f
Countess
osa? Chi? Lo vieta, lo vieta
vent her? Speak! She's modest, she's modest,
p
l'onestà. Un' abito da sposa provandoella si
that is why. A wedding dress was sent her, she has to try it
Count
p
stà, provandoella si stà Chiarissimaè la
on, she has to try it on. I grasp the situ-

Susanna
p
Ca - pi - sco qual - che
A tick - lish sit - u -
Countess
p
Brut - tis - si-ma è la co - sa, brut - tis - si-ma è la
Your shame - ful ac - cu - sa - tion, your shame - ful ac - cu -
Count
co - sa, l'a - man - te quì sa - rà, chia - ris - si-ma è la
a - tion, her lov - er hides in - side, I grasp the sit - u -
f
co - sa, veg - gia - mo co - me va, ca - pi - sco
sa - tion, it can - not be de - nied, a tick - lish
f
co - sa, chi sa co - sa sa - rà, brut -
sa - tion se - vere - ly wounds my pride, your
f
co - sa, l'a - man - te quì sa - rà,
a - tion, her lov - er hides in - side.
f
p

qual - che co - sa, veg gia - mo
sit - u - a - tion, he took us
tis - si - ma è la co - sa, chi sa co -
im - pu-dent ac - cu - sa - tion is base - less
chia - ris - si-ma è la co - sa, l'a - man - te
Dis - grace-ful sit - u - a - tion! I took them
co - me va, veg - gia - mo co - me va, ca -
by sur - prise, he took us by sur - prise. This
sa sa - rà, chi sa co - sa sa - rà, brut -
and un - wise, is base - less and un - wise! Your
quì sa - rà, quì sa - rà, chia -
by sur - prise, by sur - prise, dis -

pi - sco qual - che co - sa, quel-che co - sa, veg-
is a ver - y tick - lish sit - u - a - tion, he
ti - si-ma è la co - sa, brut-tis - si-ma è la co - sa, chi
shame - ful ac - cu - sa - tion, your shame-ful ac - cu - sa - tion is
ris - si-ma è la co - sa, chia - ris - si-ma è la co - sa, l'a-
grace - ful sit - u - a - tion, dis - grace - ful sit - u - a - tion, I
gia - mo co - me va, veg - gia - mo
took us by sur - prise, he took us
sa co - sa sa - rà, co - sa sa - rà, co -
base - less and un - wise, ver - y un - wise, ver -
man - te quì sa - rà, quì sa - rà, quì
took them by sur - prise, by sur - prise, by

co - me va, co - me va!
by — sur-prise, by sur - prise!
sa sa - rà, chi sa — co - sa — sa - rà.
y un - wise, is base-less and — un - wise.
sa - rà, quì - sa - rà.
sur - prise, by sur - prise.
fp
Countess
Fer - ma - te - vi!
Im - pos - si - ble!
Su - san - na, or via sor -
Su - san - na, what is the
fp
sen - ti - te, fer -
She can - not! Im -
ti - te, sor - ti - te,
mat - ter? Come out now!
fp
fp

ma - te - vi,
pos - si - ble!
sor - ti - re el - la non
Right now she can't ap -
io co - sì vo'!
Have - n't you heard?
fp
cresc.
può.
pear.
Dun - que par - la - te al - me - no,
Well, if I may not see you,
tr
f
p
Su - san - na, se quì sie - te!
Su - san - na, let me hear you!
Nem - men, nem - men, nem - me - no, io
You will not hear her talk - ing, ex -
cresc.

(Susanna hides in the alcove.)
v'or - di - no ta - ce - te, ta - ce - te, ta - ce - te!
press - ly I for - bid it, for - bid it, for - bid it!
p
Con-
My
p
cresc.
f
Susanna
p
O cie - lo! un pre - ci - pi - zio! Un
O Heav - ens! this is dread-ful! A
sor - te mia, giu - di - zio, con - sor - te mia, giu -
la - dy, please con - sid - er, my la - dy, please con -
p
Countess
scan - da - lo, un dis - or - di - ne, qui cer - to na - sce - rà. Con-
scan - dal, a ca - tas - tro - phe will sure - ly come to pass. Your
di - zio! giu - di - zio! giu - di - zio!
sid - er! con - sid - er! con - sid - er!

Susanna
p
O
Good
p
sor - te mio, giu - di - zio! con - sor - te mio, giu - di - zio! un
lord - ship, think it o - ver, your lord - ship, think it o - ver, no
p
Con - sor - te mia, giu - di - zio! un
My la - dy, think it o - ver, no

f
p
ciel! un pre - ci - pi - zi - o, quì cer - to na - sce - rà, o
Lord, what a ca - tas - tro - phe will sure - ly come to pass, good
f
scan - da - lo, un dis - or - di - ne, schi - viam per ca - ri - tà!
scan - dal or ca - tas - tro - phe must ev - er come to pass!
f
scan - da - lo, un dis - or - di - ne, schi - viam per ca - ri - tà!
scan - dal or ca - tas - tro - phe must ev - er come to pass!
sf
f
p

p
ciel! un pre-ci-pi - zio, un scan-da-lo, un dis - or-di-ne, quì
Lord, what a dis-as - ter, a scan-dal, a ca - tas-tro-phe will
p
Giu - di - zio! giu - di - zio! un
Be care - ful! your lord - ship, a
p
Giu - di - zio! un
Be care - ful! a
f p f p
cer - to na - sce - rà, quì cer - to na-sce-
sure - ly come to pass, will sure - ly come to
scan - da - lo, un dis - or - di-ne, schi-viam per ca-ri-
scan - dal, a ca - tas - tro-phe will sure - ly come to
scan - da - lo, un dis - or - di-ne, schi-viam per ca-ri-
scan - dal, a ca - tas - tro-phe will sure - ly come to

rà, o ciel! un pre-ci-pi - zio, un scan-da-lo, un dis-
pass; good Lord, what a dis-as - ter, a scan-dal, a ca-
tà, con-sor-te mio, giu-di - zio, un scan - da-lo, un dis-
pass; your lord-ship, think it o - ver, a scan - dal, a ca-
tà, con - sor-te mia, giu - di - zio, un scan-da-lo, un dis-
pass; my la - dy, think it o - ver, a scan-dal, a ca-
or - di - ne, quì cer - to na - sce - rà,
tas - tro-phe will sure - ly come to pass,
or - di - ne, schi-viam per ca - ri - tà, per ca - ri - tà,
tas - tro-phe will sure - ly come to pass, will come to pass,
or - di - ne, schi-viam per ca - ri - tà, per ca - ri - tà,
tas - tro-phe will sure - ly come to pass, will come to pass,
f
p

Recit.
p
quì cer - to na - sce - rà.
will sure - ly come to pass.
schi - viam per ca - ri - tà. Giu-
will sure - ly come to pass. I
schi - viam per ca - ri - tà. Giu - di - zio!
will sure - ly come to pass. I warn you!
Recit.
f
a tempo
O cie - lo! un pre - ci - pi - zio, un
Good Heav - ens! What a dis - as - ter! a
f
di - zio! con - sor - te mio, giu - di - zio, un
warn you! Your lord - ship, think it o - ver, a
f
con - sor - te mia, giu - di - zio! un
My la - dy, think it o - ver, a
a tempo
f
f
p
f
p

scan - da-lo, un dis - or - di - ne, quì cer - to na - sce - rà,
scan - dal, a ca - tas - tro - phe will sure - ly come tò pass,
scan - da-lo, un dis - or - di - ne, schi - viam per ca - ri - tà,
scan - dal, a ca - tas - tro - phe will sure - ly come to pass,
scan - da-lo, un dis - or - di - ne, schi - viam per ca - ri - tà,
scan - dal, a ca - tas - tro - phe will sure - ly come to pass,
f p f p f
quì cer - to na - sce -
will sure - ly come to
p
per ca - ri - tà, schi - viam per ca - ri -
will come to pass, will sure - ly come to
p
per ca - ri - tà, schi - viam per ca - ri -
will come to pass, will sure - ly come to
p pp

rà, qui cer - to na - sce - rà, qui
pass, will sure - ly come to pass, will
tà, schi - viam per ca - ri - tà, schi -
pass, will sure - ly come to pass, will
tà, schi - viam per ca - ri - tà, schi -
pass, will sure - ly come to pass, will
cer - to na - sce - rà.
sure - ly come to pass.
viam per ca - ri - tà.
sure - ly come to pass.
viam per ca - ri - tà.
sure - ly come to pass.
f

Recitative

Count and Countess

ren - te. At - ten - de - te pur quì... ma per - chè in tut - to sia il mio
need - ed. You will wait for me here — but be - fore leav - ing — so that all
(Locks the door to Susanna's room.)
Countess
(aside)
dub - bio di - strut - to, an - co le por - te io pri - ma chiu - de - rò. (Che im - pru -
doubts are ex - clud - ed — I shall make sure and lock all the doors. (This is
Count
den - za!) Voi la con - di - scen - den - za di ve - nir me - co a -
worse yet!) No, on sec - ond thought, be kind e - nough to come
(with feigned gaiety)
Countess
(shuddering)
vre - te; ma - da - ma, ec - co - vi il brac - cio, an - dia - mo! An -
with me. My la - dy, may I es - cort you? Here is my arm. So
Count (indicating the small room)
(Exeunt)
dia - mo! Su - san - na sta - rà quì fin - chè tor - nia - mo.
be it. Su - san - na won't mind wait - ing till we are back here!

No. 14. Aprite, presto aprite

Unlock the door and hurry!

Duettino

Susanna and Cherubino

small room, confused and breathless)
Di là, di là!
You can't, I fear!
ri - bi-le! Che gran fa - ta - li - tà!
lam - i - ty, how can I get a - way?
Che gran fa - ta - li -
I've got to get a -
Le por - te son ser - ra - te, le por - te son ser -
He locked the door from out - side, he locked the door from
tà!
way!
Le por - te son ser -
He locked the door from
ra - te, che mai sa - rà, che mai sa - rà, che mai sa -
out - side, in Heav - en's name, what can we do, what can we
ra - te, che mai sa - rà, che mai sa - rà, che mai sa -
out - side, in Heav - en's name, what can we do, what can we

rà, che mai sa - rà, che mai sa - rà, che mai sa -
do, what can we do, what can we do, what can we
rà, che mai sa - rà, che mai sa - rà, che mai sa -
do, what can we do, what can we do, what can we
rà, che mai sa - rà?
do, what can we do?
rà, che mai sa - rà? Qui per - der - si non
do, what can we do? To stay is out of
V'uc - ci - de se vi tro - va!
Then make a good sug - ges - tion!
gio - va.
ques - tion.

(going towards the window which looks out on the garden)
(as though he were go-
Veg-gia-mo un po' quì fuo-ri,
Let's see a-bout the win-dow,
dà pro-prio nel giar-
it is a-bove the
(holding him back)
Fer-ma-te, Che-ru-bi-no!
Don't do it, Che-ru-bi-no,
fer-
don't
ing to jump out)
di-no.
gar-den.
ma-te, fer-ma-te, per pie-tà!
do it, don't jump, it is too high!
(trying to free himself from her)
Qui per-der-si non
It's su-i-cide, I

Fer - ma - te, Che - ru - bi - no.
Don't do it, Che - ru - bi - no.
gio - va.
know it.
M'uc - ci - de se mi
It real - ly does not
Tropp' al - to per un sal - to, fer - ma - te, per pie -
It's much too high for jump - ing, you nev - er will get
tro - va.
mat - ter.
La - scia - mi,
No oth - er way is
tà!
by.
(releasing himself from her)
la - scia - mi!
left for me,
Pria di nuo - cer - le nel fo - co vo - le -
I would nev - er cause my la - dy an - y

(Susanna screams, sits down for a moment, and then goes to the balcony.)

Recitative

Susanna, Count, and Countess

(Enter the Countess and the Count. The Count brings a hammer and a crow-bar; after entering, he examines all the doors.)
Count
Tut-to è co-me il la-scia-i; vo-le-te dun-que a-prir voi stes-sa, o
Ev-'ry-thing as we left it! Will you your-self un-lock the door now, or
(preparing to force open the door)
Countess
(The Count
deg-gio? Ahi-mè, fer-ma-te, e a-scol-ta-te-mi un po-co, mi cre-
shall I? Just wait one mo-ment. I en-treat you to lis-ten. Do you
tosses the hammer and crow-bar onto a chair.)
Count
de-te ca-pa-ce di man-car al do-ver? Co-me vi pia-ce,
think I could fail you in my du-ty as your wife? That is the ques-tion.
en-tro quel ga-bi-net-to, chi v'è chiu-so ve-drò.
Mean-while I am pro-ceed-ing to find out who is there.
Countess (timidly and trembling)
Sì, lo ve-dre-te, ma u-di-te-mi tran-
Yes, there is some-one, but lis-ten to me

Count (incensed)
Countess (as above)
quil - lo. Non è dun - que Su - san - na? No, ma in - ve-ce è un og - get - to,
calm - ly. So it's not Su - san - na? No, but some - bod - y else
che ra - gion di so - spet - to, non vi de - ve la - sciar; per que - sta
who can give you no rea - son for sus - pi - cion or doubt. We were re -
se - ra, u - na bur - la in - no - cen - te, di far si dis - po -
hears - ing, just a harm - less di - ver - sion, a frol - ic for this
Count
ne - va, ed io vi giu - ro che l'o - nor, l'o - nes - tà... Chi è
eve - ning, and I as - sure you that my hon - or, your good faith... Who
(with increasing anger)
Countess (as above)
dun - que? di - te... l'uc - ci - de - rò. Sen - ti - te, (ah non ho
is it? say it! I'll strike him dead. Please lis - ten! (ah, I'm a -

Count
Countess
Count.
cor!) Par - la - te. Èun fan - ciul - lo. Un fan-ciul?
fraid.) Speak free - ly! It's just a child. Just a child?
Countess
Count (aside)
Sì, Che-ru-bi-no. (E mi fa-ràil de-sti - no ri-tro-var que-sto
Yes, Che-ru-bi-no. Why must I find that page-boy trail-ing my
(aloud)
paggio in o - gni lo - co!) Co - me? non è par - ti - to? scel-le -
foot-steps like a shad - ow? What? Has he not left? He de -
ra - ti! Ec-co i dub - bi spie - ga - ti, ec - co l'im -
fied me! Now I be - gin to see day - light in this con -
bro-glio, ec-co il rag - gi - ro on - de m'av-ver-te il fo - glio.
fu-sion. This is the cun-ning plot of which the let-ter warned me.

Finale of Act II

No. 15. Esci omai, garzon malnato

Out you come, don't waste a moment

Count, Countess, Susanna, Figaro, Antonio, Marcellina, Bartolo, and Basilio

Count
fam-mil cor tre-mar. E d'op-por-vi an-cor o-sa-te? e d'op-
fright-ened by your rage. And you still would dare op-pose me, and you
Countess Count Countess
por-vi an-cor o-sa-te? No, sen-ti-te. Via par-la-te. No, sen-
still would dare op-pose me? You must lis-ten! I am wait-ing. Let me
Count Countess
ti-te. Via par-la-te, par-la-te, par-la-te! Giu-ro al
tell you! I am wait-ing, the an-swer, what is it? As a
(trembling and
ciel, ch'o-gni so-spet-to, ch'o-gni so-spet-to, e lo
joke you have to take it, no bad in-ten-tion, and the

alarmed)
Count
sta-to in che il tro-va-te, sciol-to il col-lo, nu-do il pet-to... Sciol-to il
cos-tume in which you find him, o-pen col-lar, shoul-ders na-ked... O-pen
Countess
col-lo! nu-do il pet-to! se-gui-ta-te! Per ve-
col-lar! shoul-ders na-ked! Do con-tin-ue! To dis-
cresc.
f
p
stir fem-mi-nee spo-glie...
guise him as a wo-man...
Count
(Goes toward the small room, then turns around)
Ah! com-pren-do, in-de-gna mo-glie, mi vo'
How in-de-cent, how out-ra-geous! for his
(forcefully)
Mi fa tor-to quel tra-spor-to, m'ol-trag-gia-te a du-bi-
You of-fend me most se-vere-ly by ac-cus-ing me this
tos-to ven-di-car, ah! com-pren-do in-de-gna mo-glie, mi vo'
bold-ness he shall pay! How in-de-cent, how out-ra-geous! for his
f
3
p

tar; mi fa tor - to quel tra-spor - to, m'ol - trag -
way, you of - fend me most se - vere - ly, most se -
to - sto ven - di - car; ah! com - pren - do in - de - gna
bold - ness he shall pay! How in - de - cent, how out -
giа - te, m'ol - trag - gia - te a du - bi - tar, m'ol - trag - gia - te a du - bi -
vere - ly, by ac - cus - ing me this way, by ac - cus - ing me this
(approaching the small room)
mo - glie, mi vo' to - sto ven - di - car, mi vo' to - sto ven - di -
ra - geous! for his bold - ness he shall pay, for his bold - ness he shall
tar, m'ol - trag - gia - te a du - bi - tar.
way, by ac - cus - ing me this way.
car, mi vo' to - sto ven - di - car,
pay, for his bold - ness he shall pay.
cresc.

(Gives him the key.)
E - gli è in-no - cen-te! e - gli è in-no-
He is not guilt-y, he is not
(turning back)
Quà la chia-ve! quà la chia-ve!
Let me en-ter! Let me en-ter!
Count
cen - te! voi sa - pe - te. Non so nien - te! Va lon -
guilt - y! You know bet - ter! I know noth-ing! Go a -
tan dagli oc - chi mie - i! Un' in - fi - da, un' em - pia se - i, e mi
way at once and leave me, you're un-faith - ful and de-ceived me, you have
Countess
cer - chi d'in - fa - mar, e mi cer - chi d'in - fa - mar.
cov - ered me with shame, you have cov - ered me with shame. I
cresc.

Va - do,
sì,
ma. . .
leave you,
yes. . .
but. . .
Count
Non a - scol - to,
I won't lis - ten,
ma. . .
but. . .
Recit.
Non son re - a!
I am blame-less!
Non a - scol - to.
I won't lis - ten,
Vel leg-go in
I don't be-
Recit.
Ah! la
Ah, his
tempo
vol - to!
lieve you!
Mo - ra,
I shall
mo - ra,
kill him.
p a tempo

cie - ca ge - lo - si - a, qual - che ec -
ear is deaf to rea - son, jeal - ous
mo - ra, mo - ra,
I shall kill him,
ces - so gli fa far. Ah! la cie - ca ge - lo -
rage has made him blind! Ah, his ear is deaf to
mo - ra, mo - ra, e più non si - a, ria ca -
he must die for his trea-son! Noth - ing
si - a, qual-che ec - ces - so gli fa far. Mia fa
rea - son, jeal-ous rage has made him blind. What sus -
gion, ria ca - gion del mio pe - nar! Ah! com - pren - do!
less, noth-ing less can ease my mind! Now I know you!
f p f p

tor- to, quel tra- spor - to!
pi- cion! What in- jus - tice!
in - de- gna mo- glie. Mo - ra,
Un-worth - y wo - man, I shall
f p f p
Ah, la cie- ca_ ge- lo - si - a,
Ah, his ear is_ deaf to rea - son,
mo - ra, mo - ra,
kill him, I shall
qual - che ec - ces- so- gli fa far, Ah! la
jeal - ous rage has made him blind. Ah, his
mo - ra, mo - ra, mo - ra, e più non si - a,
kill him! He must die ___ for his trea- son,

cie - ca ge - lo - si - a, qual-che ec - ces - so gli fa far, qual-che ec-
ear is deaf to rea - son, jeal - ous rage has made him blind, jeal - ous
ria ca - gion, ria ca - gion del mio pe - nar, ria ca-
noth - ing less, noth-ing less can ease my mind, noth - ing
f
ces - so gli fa far, qual - che ec - ces - so gli fa far, qual - che ec-
rage has made him blind, jeal - ous rage has made him blind, jeal - ous
gion del mio pe - nar, ria ca - gion del mio pe - nar, del
less can ease my mind, noth - ing less can ease my mind, can
p
f
p
ces - so gli fa far!
rage has made him blind!
(Opens the door; Susanna gravely issues from the door-way and remains there.)
mio pe - nar.
ease my mind!
f

Count
(astonished)
Countess
(astonished)
Su - san-na!
Su - san-na!
Su - san-na!
Su - san-na!
Andante con moto
Susanna
Si - gno-re!
Your lord-ship!
(ironically)
Cos' è quel stu - po - re? Il bran-do pren - de-te, il
You seem so be-wild-ered! The wick-ed of - fend-er has
paggio uc - ci - de - te! Quel pag-gio mal - na - to ve - de - te - lo
come to sur - ren-der, your treach-er - ous rí - val is stand-ing right

quà, quel pag - gio mal - na - to ve - de - te - lo
here, your treach - er - ous ri - val is stand - ing right
mf
p
quà.
here.
Countess (aside)
Che sto - ria è mai
I can't un - der-
Count (aside)
Che sco - la! la
They fooled me, this
Susanna (aside)
Con-fu-sa han la tes - ta, non san co - me va, con-fu-sa han la
How all this has hap-pened they can-not ex-plain, how all this has
que - sta, Su - san - na v'è là! che
stand it, Su - san - na, ex - plain! I
tes - ta gi - ran - do mi va, che
thing is con - fus - ing my brain, they

te - sta, non san co - me va, con-fu-sa han la te - sta, non san co - me
hap-pened they can-not ex - plain, how all this has hap-pened they can-not ex -
sto-ria è mai que - sta, Su - san - na v'è
can't un - der - stand it, Su - san - na, ex -
sco - la! la te - sta gi - ran - do mi
fooled me, this thing is con - fus - ing my
va. Guar - da - te! Qui a - sco - so sa -
plain. You mean, sir, he still might be
là!
plain!
va. Sei so - la?
brain. How ev - er...
rà, guar - da - te! quì a - sco - so sa -
there, all right then, he still might be
Guar - dia - mo! guar - dia - mo! quì a - sco - so sa -
All right then, all right then, he still might be
mf
p

rà, guar - da - te! guar - da - te! quì a - sco - so sa -
there. Why don't you go look then, he still might be
rà, guar - dia - mo! quì a - sco - so sa -
there. I'll look then, he still might be
mf
p
Allegro
Countess
rà. Su - san - na, son mor - ta, il fia - to mi
there. Su - san - na, I'm wear - y, I'm breath-less with
(The Count goes into the small room.)
rà.
there.
Allegro
Susanna (Quickly indicates to the Countess the window from which Cherubino leaped.)
man - ca. Più lie - ta, più fran - ca, in sal - vo è di
ter - ror. Don't wor - ry, be cheer - ful, the page is not
già.
there.
Count (Comes out of the small room in confusion.)
Che sba - glio mai pre - si! che sba - glio mai
How bad - ly mis - tak - en! Com - plete - ly mis -
f
p

pre - si! Ap - pe - na lo cre - do. Se a tor - to v'of -
tak - en. I scarce - ly be - lieve it.. If I did of -
f
p
fe - si, per - do - no vi chie - do, per - do - no vi
fend you, I beg your for - give - ness, I'm sure you will
chie - do; ma far bur - la
give it. But such cru - el
f
si - mi - le è poi cru - del -
es - ca - pades are quite out of

Susanna
Le vo - stre fol - li - e non mer - tan pie -
Your fool - ish be - hav - ior can mer - it no
Countess (with her handkerchief at her mouth to conceal her agitation)
tà. Le vo - stre fol - li - e non mer - tan pie -
place. Your fool - ish be - hav - ior can mer - it no
tà, le vo - stre fol - li - e non mer - tan pie -
grace, your fool - ish be - hav - ior can mer - it no
tà, le vo - stre fol - li - e non mer - tan pie -
grace, your fool - ish be - hav - ior can mer - it no
Countess (gradually recovering from her confusion)
tà. Nol di - te! men-
grace! Don't say it! You're
Count
tà. Io v'a - mo! vel giu - ro!
grace! I love you! I swear it!

(forcefully and angrily)
ti - te! Son l'em - pia, l'in -
ly - ing, I'm wick - ed, un -
f
fi - da, che o - gno - ra v'in -
faith - ful, and al - ways de -
Count
gan - na. Quell' i - ra, Su - san - na, m'a - i - ta a cal -
ceive you. Please help me, Su - san - na, her an - ger to
p
Susanna
mar. Co - sì si con - dan - na chi può so - spet - tar, co - sì si con -
calm. Your jeal - ous sus - pi - cion has done all this harm, your jeal - ous sus -

Countess (resentfully)
dan - na chi può so - spet - tar. A - dun - que la fe - de
pi - cion has done all this harm. My love, al - ways faith - ful,
f
d'un' a - ni-ma a - man - te, sì fie - ra mer -
so true and un - swerv - ing, is sure - ly de -
Count
ce - de do - ve - va spe - rar? Quell' i - ra, Su -
serv - ing of bet - ter re - ward. Oh, help me, Su -
p
Susanna
san - na, m'a - i - ta a cal - mar. Co - sì si con -
san - na, her an - ger to calm. Your jeal - ous sus -

dan-na chi può so-spet-tar, co-sì si con-dan-na chi può so-spet-tar.
pi-cion has done all this harm, your jeal-ous sus-pi-cion has done all this harm.
(beseechingly)
Count (beseechingly)
Countess
Si-gno-ra! Ro-si-na! Cru-
My la-dy. Ro-si-na! You
(to the Count)
de-le! più quel-la non so-no! Ma il mi-se-ro og-
trai-tor! Those days are for-got-ten! I once was con-
cresc.
f
p
get-to del vo-stro ab-ban-do-no, che a-ve-te di-
tent-ed, a-dored by my lov-er, but now I'm tor-

Susanna
Con - fu - so, pen -
De - ject - ed, re -
let - to di far di - spe - rar. Cru -
ment - ed and scorned by my lord. You
Count
Con - fu - so, pen - ti - to, son
De - ject - ed, re - pent - ant, I

ti - to, è trop - po pu - ni - to, è trop - po pu -
pent - ant, he begs for your par - don, don't har - bor re -
de - le! cru - de - le, sof - frir sì gran
trai - tor! You trai - tor, I'll nev - er for -
trop - po pu - ni - to, ah! son trop - po pu -
beg your for - give - ness, ah! don't har - bor re -

ni - to, ab - bia - te pie - tà, ab bia - te, ab -
sent - ment, be kind and for - give, have mer - cy, be -
tor - to, quest' al - ma non sa, ah! no, quest'
give you as long as I live, ah, no, as
ni - to, ab - bia - te pie - tà, ab - bia - te, ab -
sent - ment, have mer - cy, for - give, have mer - cy, be
cresc.
bia - te pie - tà.
kind and for - give.
al - ma non sa.
long as I live.
Fu
To
bia - te pie - tà.
kind and for - give.
Mai l pag - gio rin - chiu - so?
But what of the page then?
f
p

Count
sol per pro - var - vi.
test and pro - voke you.
Ma i tre - mi - ti, i
Your fright and em -
f
p
Countess
Count
pal-pi - ti? Fu sol per bur - lar - vi.
bar-rass-ment? Was just to mis - lead you.
Ma un fo - glio sì
But what does the
Susanna
Di Fi - ga - ro è il fo - glio, e a voi per Ba -
By Fi - ga - ro writ - ten and sent through Ba -
Countess
Count
bar - ba - ro?
let - ter mean?

si - lio.
si - lio.
Per - do - no non
If you_ want for -
si - lio.
si - lio.
Per - do - no non
If you_ want for -
Ah! per - fi - di io vo - glio. . . io vo - glio. . .
What in-fam-y, how dare they. . . how dare they. . .
f
p
mer - ta chia - gli al - tri nol da, per - do - no non mer - ta chi a - gli al - tri nol
give-ness, you, too,_ must for - give, if you want for - give-ness, you, too, must for -
mer - ta chia - gli al - tri nol da, per - do - no non mer - ta chi a - gli al - tri nol
give-ness, you, too, must for - give, if you want for - give-ness, you, too, must for -

da.
give.
Count (tenderly)
da. Eb - ben se vi pia - ce, com - mu - ne è la
give. If all have con - sent - ed, the quar - rel is
pa - ce; Ro - si - na in - fles - si - bi - le con me non sa -
end - ed. Ro - si - na, I beg of you, this time to for -
Countess
rà. Ah quan - to, Su - san - na, son dol - ce di
give. I feel it, Su - san - na, I weak - en al -
co - re! Di don - ne al fu - ro - re chi più cre - de -
read - y; why is it that wo - men can nev - er be

Susanna
ra? Co-gli uo-min, si-gno-ra, gi-ra-te, vol-ge-te,
firm? When men are in ques-tion, how-ev-er you treat them,
p
f
ve-dre-te che o-gno-ra si ca-de poi là, gi-ra-te, vol-
you nev-er de-feat them, as hard as you scheme, how-ev-er you
cresc.
ge-te, vol-ge-te, gi-ra-te, ve-dre-te che o-
treat them, you nev-er de-feat them, you nev-er de-
Count (tenderly)
Countess
gno-ra si ca-de poi là. Guar-da-te-mi! In-
feat them, how hard you may scheme. You par-don me? I

Count
Countess
Count (covering her hand with
gra - to! Guar - da - te - mi! In - gra - to! Guar - da - te - mi, ho
can - not! You par - don me? I can - not! I treat - ed you un -
fp
fp
kisses)
tor - to, e mi pen - to.
just - ly, I am sor - ry.
pp

Susanna sotto voce
Da que - sto mo - men - to, quest' al - ma a co -
He means it sin - cere - ly, he hopes from now
Countess sotto voce
Da que - sto mo - men - to, quest' al - ma a co -
He means it sin - cere - ly, he hopes from now
Count sotto voce
Da que - sto mo - men - to, quest' al - ma a co -
I mean it sin - cere - ly, I hope from now

cresc.
no - scer-la ap - pren - der po - trà,
on his mis - take to re - deem.
cresc.
f
no - scer-mi ap - pren - der po - trà, quest' al - ma a co -
on his mis - take to re - deem. He hopes from now
cresc.
f
no - scer-vi ap - pren - der po - trà, quest' al - ma a co -
on my mis - take to re - deem. I hope from now
cresc.
f
f
p
quest' al - ma a co - no - scer-la ap - pren - der po -
He hopes from now on his mis - take to re -
p
no - scer-mi ap - pren - der po -
on his mis - take to re -
p
no - scer-vi ap - pren - der po -
on my mis - take to re -
p

f
p
f
trà, a co - no - scer-la ap - pren - der po - trà, a co -
deem, his mis - take he will full - y re - deem, all his
trà, a co - no - scer-mi ap - pren - der po - trà, a co -
deem, all his er - rors he will full - y re - deem, all his
trà, a co - no - scer-vi ap - pren - der po - trà, a co -
deem, all my er - rors I will full - y re - deem, all my
no - scer - la ap - pren - der po - trà.
er - rors he will full - y re - deem.
no - scer - mi ap - pren - der po - trà.
er - rors he will full - y re - deem.
no - scer - vi ap - pren - der po - trà.
er - rors I will full - y re - deem.

(Enter Figaro.)
Allegro
Figaro
Si - gno - re; di fuo - ri son
Dear mas - ter, just lis - ten, the
già i suo - na - to - ri,
mu - sic is sound - ing,
le trom - be sen -
the trum - pets are
ti - te,
blar - ing,
i pif - fe - ri u - di - te, tra
the fid - dles are play - ing, the
can - ti, tra bal - li de' vo - stri vas - sal - li, cor - ria - mo, vo -
ech - oes are ring - ing, the peo - ple are sing - ing, the wed - ding pro -

(taking Susanna by the arm and about
lia - mo le noz-ze a com - pir, cor - ria - mo, vo - lia - mo le
ces - sion is read - y to start, the wed- ding pro - ces - sion is
p f p f p cresc.
to leave)
Count (detaining him)
Figaro
noz - ze a com - pir. Pian, pia - no, men fret - ta. La
read - y to start. There's time, so don't hur - ry. The
f p
Count
tur - ba m'a - spet - ta. Pian, pia - no, men fret - ta, un
crowd is im - pa - tient. There's time, so don't hur - ry, just
p
dub - bio to - glie - te - mi in pria di par - tir, in pria di par -
one ex - pla - na - tion be - fore we de - part, be - fore we de -
tr

Susanna sotto voce
La co - sa'e sca - bro - sa, com'
A new com - pli - ca - tion with
Countess sotto voce
La co - sa'e sca - bro - sa, com'
A new com - pli - ca - tion with
sotto voce
tir. Con ar - te le
part. I know that this
Figaro sotto voce
La co - sa'e sca. - bro - sa, com'
A new com - pli - ca - tion with
ha da fi - nir? la co -
which to con - tend, a bad
ha da fi - nir? la co -
which to con - tend, a bad
car - te con - vien qui sco - prir, con ar - te le car - te con -
ruse will ac - com - plish my end, with this com - pli - ca - tion they
ha da fi - nir? la co -
which to con - tend, a bad

sa'è sca - bro - sa, la co - sa'è sca -
sit - u - a - tion, a bad sit - u -
sa'è sca - bro - sa, la co - sa'è sca -
sit - u - a - tion, a bad sit - u -
vien qui sco - prir, con ar - te le car - te con - vien qui sco -
can - not con - tend, I know that this ruse will ac - com-plish my
sa'è sca - bro - sa, la co - sa'è sca -
sit - u - a - tion, a bad sit - u -
bro - sa, com' ha da fi - nir, com' ha
a - tion, but how will it end, but how
bro - sa, com' ha da fi - nir, com' ha
a - tion, but how will it end, but how
prir, con ar - te le car - te con -
end, with this com-pli - ca - tion they
bro - sa, com' ha da fi - nir, com' ha
a - tion, but how will it end, but how

da fi - nir, com' ha da fi - nir, com'
will it end, but how will it end, but
da fi - nir, com' ha da fi - nir, com'
will it end, but how will it end, but
vien quì sco - prir, con ar - te le
can - not con - tend, I know that this
da fi - nir, com' ha da fi - nir, com'
will it end, but how will it end, but
ha da fi - nir?
how will it end?
ha da fi - nir?
how will it end?
car - te con - vien quì sco - prir.
ruse will ac - com - plish my end.
ha da fi - nir?
how will it end?

Count
Andante
(Shows him the letter)
Co-no-sce-te, si-gnor Fi-ga-ro, que-sto fo-glio chi ver-
Kind-ly tell me, mis-ter Fi-ga-ro, did you ev-er see this
f
p
Figaro (pretending to examine it)
gò? Nol co-no-sco, nol co-
note? Nev-er saw it, nev-er
tr
Susanna
Nol co-no-sci?
Nev-er saw it?
Countess
Nol co-
Nev-er
Count
Figaro
no-sco!
saw it.
No!
No!

Nol co - no - sci?
Nev - er saw it?
no - sci?
saw it?
Nol co - no - sci?
Nev - er saw it?
Nol co - no - sci, nol co - no - sci?
Nev - er saw it? Nev - er saw it?
No, no, no, no,
No! no! no, no,
cresc.
f
Susanna
Countess
E nol de - sti a Don Ba - si - lio? Per re -
Figaro
Did - n't give it to Ba - si - lio? To de -
no!
no!
p
Count
Susanna
car - lo... Tu c'in - ten - di?
liv - er... What a - bout it?
E non
You don't
Figaro
Oi - bò, oi - bò!
Oh, no, oh, no!
f
f
p

Countess
Count
sai del da-me-ri-no— Che sta-se-ra nel giar-di-no? Già ca-
know a-bout a lov-er... Who this eve-ning in the gar-den... You re-
pi-sci?
mem-ber?
Figaro
Io non lo sò.
Why, not at all.
Cer-chi in-van di-fe-sa e
Stop e-vad-ing and de-
scu-sa, il tuo cef-fo già t'ac-
ny-ing, I can see that you are

cu - sa, ve - do ben che vuoi men -
ly - ing, it is writ - ten in your
Susanna
Il ta - len - to a - guz - zi in -
What's the use of all the
Countess
Il ta - len - to a - guz - zi in -
What's the use of all the
Figaro
tir. Men - te il cef - fo, io già non men - to,
face. Well, my face may lie, but I don't,
va - no, pa - le - sa - to ab - biam l'ar - ca - no, non v'è
rus - es, we can see through your ex - cus - es, and the
va - no, pa - le - sa - to ab - biam l'ar - ca - no, non v'è
rus - es, we can see through your ex - cus - es, and the
men - te il cef - fo, io già non men - to.
well, my face may lie, but I don't.

nul - la da ri - dir.
truth you can't de - ny.
Count
nul - la da ri - dir. Che ri - spon - di?
truth you can't de - ny. What's your an - swer?
Figaro
Nien - te,
Noth - ing,
Susanna
Eh via che - ta - ti, ba -
There's no point in tell - ing
Dun - que ac - cor - di?
You ad - mit it?
nien - te!
noth - ing.
Non ac - cor - do!
No, I will not!
lor - do, eh via che - ta - ti, ba - lor - do; la bur - let - ta ha da fi -
sto - ries, there's no point in tell - ing sto - ries, you have car - ried things too
Countess
Eh via che - ta - ti, ba - lor - do; la bur - let - ta ha da fi -
There's no point in tell - ing sto - ries, you have car - ried things too
cresc.

nir, la bur-let-ta ha da fi - nir.
far, you have car-ried things too far.
nir, la bur-let-ta ha da fi - nir.
far, you have car-ried things too far.
Figaro
Per fi- nir la lie - ta -
In the - at - ri - cal tra -
f
p
(taking Su-
men - te, e all' u - san - za te - a - tra - le, un' a -
di - tion, let us have a hap - py end - ing, with a
tr
sanna by the arm)
zion ma - tri - mo - nia - le le fa - re - mo o - ra se -
wed - ding cel - e - bra - tion when the fi - nal cur - tain
tr

Susanna sotto voce
Deh si - gnor, nol con - tra - sta - te, con - so - la - te i miei de -
Won't you give us your per - mis - sion, say the word we long to
Countess sotto voce
Deh si - gnor, - nol con - tra - sta - te, con - so - la - te i lor de -
Won't you give - them your per - mis - sion, say the word - they long to
sotto voce
guir. Deh si - gnor, nol con - tra - sta - te, con - so - la - te i miei de -
falls. Won't you give us your per - mis - sion, say the word we long to
f
p
sir, deh si - gnor, - nol con - tra - sta - te, con - so -
hear, won't you give - us your per - mis - sion, say the
sir, - deh si - gnor, nol con - tra - sta - te, con - so -
hear, - won't you give them your per - mis - sion, say the
Count (aside)
(Mar - cel - li - na, Mar - cel - li - na! quan - to
(Mar - cel - li - na, Mar - cel - li - na! you are
sir, con - so - la - te, con - so -
hear, make us hap - py, say the

la - tei miei de - sir, deh si - gnor, nol con - tra -
word we long to_ hear, let us two at last be
la - tei lor de - sir, deh si - gnor,_ nol con - tra -
word they long to_ hear, let the two_ at last be
tar - dia com - pa - rir! Mar - cel - li - na, Mar - cel - li - na!
late in get - ting here, Mar - cel - li - na, Mar - cel - li - na!
la - tei miei de - sir, deh si - gnor, nol con - tra -
word we long to hear, let us two at last be
mfp
sta - te, con - so - la - tei miei de - sir, deh si -
mar - ried, say the word we long to hear, let us
sta - te, con - so - la - tei lor de - sir,_ deh si -
mar - ried, say the word_ they long to hear,_ let the
quan - to tar - dia com - pa - rir! Mar - cel -
you are late in get - ting here. Mar - cel -
sta - te, con - so - la - tei miei de - sir,
mar - ried, say the word we long to hear,
f

gnor, nol con - tra - sta - te, con - so - la - te i miei de -
two at last be mar - ried, say the word we long to
gnor, nol con - tra - sta - te, con - so - la - te i lor de -
two at last be mar - ried, say the word they long to
li - na, Mar - cel - li - na! quan - to tar - di a com - pa -
li - na! Mar - cel - li - na! you are late in get - ting
con - so - la - te, con - so - la - te i miei de -
make us hap - py, say the word we long to
Allegro molto
sir, con - so - la - te i miei de - sir.
hear, say the word we long to hear.
sir, con - so - la - te i lor de - sir.
hear, say the word they long to hear.
rir, quan - to tar - di a com - pa - rir.)
here, you are late in get - ting here.)
sir, con - so - la - te i miei de - sir.
hear, say the word we long to hear.
Allegro molto

(Enter Antonio, the gardener, excitedly, with a pot of trampled geraniums.)
Antonio (enraged)
Ah! si - gnor! si - gnor!
Ah, my lord! my lord!
Count (anxiously)
Co - sa'e sta - to?
What has hap-pened?
Antonio
Che in-so - len - za! chi'l fe - ce? chi fu?
Who has dared, who has done this to me?
Susanna
Co - sa di - ci, cos' hai, co-sa'e na - to?
What's the mat - ter with you, what has hap - pened?
Countess
Co - sa di - ci, cos' hai, co-sa'e na - to?
What's the mat - ter with you, what has hap - pened?
Count
Co - sa di - ci, cos' hai, co-sa'e na - to?
What's the mat - ter with you, what has hap - pened?
Figaro
Co - sa di - ci, cos' hai, co-sa'e na - to?
What's the mat - ter with you, what has hap - pened?
Antonio (as above)
A - scol -
I won't

Via par - la, dì su?
What have you to say?
Via par - la, dì su?
What have you to say?
Via par - la, dì su?
What have you to say?
Via par - la, dì su?
What have you to say?
Via par - la, dì su?
What have you to say?
Via par - la, dì su?
What have you to say?
Figaro
Antonio
Figaro
ta - te! Via par - la, dì su? A - scol - ta - te! Via par - la, dì su?
have it! What have you to say? I won't have it! What have you to say?
f
p
f
3
3
Antonio
Dal bal - co - ne che guar - da in giar -
From the win - dow that looks on the
p
di - no, mil - le co - se o - gni dì git - tar veg - gio, e poc'
gar - den ev - 'ry day they throw down man - y ob - jects, but to -

an - zi, può dar - si di peg - gio, vi-di un uom, si-gnor mio, git-tar
day it is real - ly the lim - it, they have thrown a whole man to the
Count (with vivacity)
Antonio (showing the pot)
Count
giù. Dal bal-co-ne? Ve-de-te i ga - ro-fa-ni! In giar -
ground! From the win-dow? Just look at the ge - ra-ni-ums. In - to the
Susanna (softly, to Figaro)
(aside)
Fi - ga-ro, all' er - ta! Co -
Fi - ga-ro, help us! Our
Countess (softly, to Figaro)
(aside)
Fi - ga-ro, all' er - ta! Co -
Fi - ga-ro, help us! Our
Antonio
Count
Figaro (aside)
di - no? Sì! Co - sa sen - to? Co -
gar- den? Yes. Do you mean it? Our
cresc.

f (aloud)
stui ci scon-cer-ta: quel bri-a-co, che
plan will be ru-ined! Is this drunk-ard quite
f (aloud)
stui ci scon-cer-ta: quel bri-a-co, che
plan will be ru-ined! Is this drunk-ard quite
f (aloud)
stui ci scon-cer-ta: quel bri-a-co, che
plan will be ru-ined! Is this drunk-ard quite
p
f
vie-ne a far qui?
out of his mind?
vie-ne a far qui?
out of his mind?
Count (to Antonio, fiercely)
vie-ne a far qui? Dun-que un uom... ma dov' è, dov' è
out of his mind? And this man, what be-came of him
p
Antonio
gi-to? Rat-to, rat-to il bir-bo-ne è fu-gi-to e ad un
lat-er? He went by like a shot from a can-non, in a

Susanna (softly, to Figaro)
Sai che il pag - gio...
Che-ru - bi - no..
Figaro (softly, to Susanna)
trat - to di vi - sta m'u - scì.
flash he had left me be - hind.
So tut - to, lo
I know it, I
(laughing aloud)
Count
Figaro
vi - di. Ah! ah! ah! ah!
saw him, ha, ha, ha, ha!
Ta - ci
Qui - et
là! Ah! ah! ah!
there! Ha, ha, ha,
Count
ah!
ha!
ah! ah! ah! ah!
ha, ha, ha, ha!
Ta - ci
Hold your
Antonio
Co - sa ri - di?
What's so fun - ny?
Co - sa
What's so
f
p
f
p
f

là! ta - ci là! ta - ci là!
tongue, all of you! hold your tongue!
Figaro
Tu sei
Are you
ri - di? co - sa ri - di? co - sa ri - di?
fun - ny, what's so fun - ny, what's so fun - ny?
cot - to dal sor - ger del dì, tu sei cot - to dal sor - ger del
tip - sy from morn - ing till night, are you tip - sy from morn - ing till
Count
dì. Or ri - pe - ti - mi, ri - pe - ti - mi: un uom dal bal-
night? Now re - peat what you just said to me! He fell from the

Antonio
Count
Antonio
co - ne? Dal bal - co - ne. In giar - di - no? In giar -
win - dow? From the win - dow. On the flow - ers? On the
Susanna
Ma si - gno - re, se in lui par - la il
But, your lord - ship, he's drunk, can't you
Countess
Ma si - gno - re, se in lui par - la il
But, your lord - ship, he's drunk, can't you
Figaro
di - no. Ma si - gno - re, se in lui par - la il
flow - ers. But, your lord - ship, he's drunk, can't you
f
vi - no.
see it?
vi - no.
see it?
Count
vi - no. Se - gui pu - re, se - gui pu - re: nè in vol - to il ve -
see it? Just con - tin - ue! Tell your sto - ry! You saw what he
f
tr
p

(softly, to Figaro)
p
O - là, Fi - ga-ro, a-scol-ta! Fi - ga-ro,a-
Look out, Fi - ga-ro, help us! Fi - ga-ro,
p (softly, to Figaro)
O - là, Fi - ga-ro,a-
Look out, Fi - ga-ro,
Antonio
Count
Antonio
de - sti? No, nol vi - di. No? Nol
looked like? No, I did not. No? I
scol-ta!
help us!
scol-ta!
help us!
Figaro (to Antonio)
vi - di. Via pian - gio - ne, sta zit - tou - na vol - ta! Per tre
could not. Will you ev - er be fin - ished com-plain - ing! Such a

(pointing contemptuously to the geraniums)
sol - di far tan - to tu - mul - to; giac-chè il fat - to non può sta-re oc -
fuss o - ver noth - ing what - ev - er. If the truth can no long - er be
cul - to, so - noio stes - so sal - ta - to di lì, so - no io
hid - den, I my - self was the man whom you saw, I my -
cresc.
Susanna (aside)
Che te - sta! che in -
How bril-liant! How
Countess (aside)
Che te - sta! che in -
How bril-liant! How
Count
Figaro
stes - so sal - ta - to di lì. Chi! voi stes - so? Che stu -
self was the man whom you saw. You! And why? What sur -
f
p
f

ge - gno!
che te - sta! che in - ge - gno!
clev - er!
How bril-liant! How clev - er!
ge - gno!
che te - sta! che in - ge - gno!
clev - er!
How bril-liant! How clev - er!
Antonio
Figaro
por! Chi! voi stes - so? Che stu - por! che stu -
prise! You! And why? What sur - prise! What sur-
p
f
p
Count
Antonio
por! Già cre - der nol pos - so. Co - me mai di - ven - ta - sti sì
prise! I can - not be - lieve it! In that case you have grown ver - y
fp
Count
Già cre - der nol pos - so, nol pos - so.
That sounds un - like - ly, un - like - ly.
gras - so! Do - po il
quick - ly. Af - ter
f
p

Figaro
A chi sal - ta suc - ce - de co -
When one jumps one be-comes ver - y
sal - to non fo - sti co - sì.
jump - ing you looked ver - y small.
Susanna (aside)
Ed in - si - ste quel paz - zo?
Who be-lieves all this non - sense?
Countess (aside)
Ed in - si - ste quel paz - zo?
Who be-lieves all this non - sense?
Figaro Antonio
Count (to Antonio)
sì. Chi'l di - reb - be! Tu che
small. You don't say so! Come, de -
f
p
Count
(violently)
Susanna (aside)
p
di - ci? Che-ru - bin? Ma - le -
scribe him! Che-ru - bin? I can't
Antonio
Countess (aside)
A me par - ve il ra - gaz - zo! Ma - le -
He looked like a young - ster! I can't
f
p
cresc.
fp

det - to! ma - le - det - to!
bear it! I can't bear it!
Figaro
det - to! ma - le - det - to! Es - so ap - pun - to, es - so ap-
bear it! I can't bear it! Che - ru - bi - no! Che - ru-
(ironically)
pun - to, da Si - vi - glia a ca - val - lo qui giun - to, da Si -
bi - no, who re - turned from Se-ville on horse-back, for it's
Antonio (with stupid simplicity)
vi - glia ov' ei for - se sa - rà. Que - sto no, que - sto no, che il ca -
there he was sent by the Count. No, no, no, he was not on
Count
val - lo io non vi - di sal - ta - re di là. Che pa -
horse-back, he jumped out the win - dow on foot! Don't be

Susanna (aside)
Co - me mai, giu-sto ciel, fi-ni-
Heav - en knows what will come out of
Countess (aside)
Co - me mai, giu-sto ciel, fi-ni-
Heav - en knows what will come out of
zien - za! Fi-niam que-sto bal - lo!
fool - ish! Let's get to the point!
rà.
this!
rà.
this!
(to Figaro, fiercely)
Figaro (innocently)
Count
Dun - que tu? Sal - tai giù. Ma per-
It was you? That is true. But what
Figaro
Count
Figaro (indicat-
chè? Il ti-mor. Che ti-mor? Là rin-
for? I was scared. You were scared? I had

ing the maid's room)
chiu - so, a-spet-tan - do quel ca - ro vi - set - to, tip-pe,
come here and was wait - ing to see my Su-san - na, when I
tap - pe, un su-sur - ro fuor d'u - so, voi gri -
heard an-gry voi - ces from out - side; you were
cresc.
f
da - ste, lo scrit - to bi-gliet-to, sal-tai giù dal ter-
rag-ing, I thought of my let-ter; scared to death, I jumped
p
(Pretends that his foot hurts him.)
a piacere
ro - re con-fu - so, e stra - vol - to m'ho un ner - vo del
down from the win - dow and I twist - ed my foot when I
f
p
colla voce

Andante ma non troppo
pië.
fell.
Antonio
Vo-stre
Then these
p
Count (Takes them from him.)
O - là, por-gi-le a me!
O - ho! Give them to me!
(handing Figaro some folded papers)
dun-que sa-ran que-ste car - te, che per - de - ste.
pa-pers I found in the gar - den must be yours?
Figaro
p
So - no in
Now I'm
Susanna (softly, to Figaro)
Fi - ga-ro, all' er - ta! Fi - ga-ro, all'
Fi - ga - ro, help us! Fi - ga - ro,
Countess (softly, to Figaro)
Fi - ga-ro, all' er - ta! Fi - ga-ro, all'
Fi - ga - ro, help us! Fi - ga - ro,
(softly, to the Countess and Susanna)
trap - po-la, so - no in trap - po-la.
in for it, now I'm in for it.

er - ta!
help us!
Count (Opens the paper and immediately folds it again.)
er - ta!
help us!
Di - te un pò, que - sto fo - glio cos'
Do you know what this pa - per may
Figaro (taking some papers out of his pocket)
è? To - sto, to - sto, n'ho tan - te, a - spet -
be? Yes, I know it, I know it, just a
Antonio
Figaro
ta - te! Sa - rà for - se il som - ma - rio dei de - bi - ti? No, la
mo - ment! Well, per - haps it's a list of his cred - i - tors! No, I
cresc.
f
p
Count (to Figaro) (to Antonio)
li - sta de - gli o - sti. Par - la - te! e tu la - scia - lo.
don't buy on cred - it! Speak up now. And you let him be.
cresc.
f
p

Susanna
La - scia - lo, e par - ti.
Off with you, An - to - nio!
Countess
La - scia - lo, e par - ti.
Off with you, An - to - nio!
Figaro
La - scia - mi, e par - ti.
Off with you, An - to - nio!
Antonio
Par - to si, ma se tor - no a tro -
I will go, but the next time I
cresc.
f p
la - scia - lo,
Off with you!
la - scia - lo,
Off with you!
la - scia - lo,
Off with you!
la - scia - lo,
Off with you!
Count
la - scia - lo,
Off with you!
la - scia - lo,
Off with you!
Figaro
Van - ne, van - ne, non te - mo di te,
Go a - way, I'm not fright-ened of you!
Antonio
var - ti...
see you...
par - to
I will
f p
f p

la - scia - lo, e par - -
off with you, good rid - -
la - scia - lo, e par - -
off with you, good rid - -
la - scia - lo, e par - -
off with you, good rid - -
van - ne, van - ne, non te - mo di
go a - way, I'm not fright - ened of
si, ma se tor-no a tro - var - ti...
go, but the next time I see you...
(Exit Antonio.)
cresc.
Susanna
ti!
dance!
Countess
ti!
dance!
O
Good
Count
(Re-opens the paper and folds it again quickly.)
(to Figaro)
ti!
dance!
Dun - que?
Well now?
Figaro
ti!
you!
f p

Susanna
(softly, to Figaro)
Giu - sti Dei! la pa - ten - te!
That is right, his com - mis - sion!
Countess
(softly, to Susanna)
ciel! la pa - ten - te del pag - gio!
Heav-ens, the pa - ge's com - mis - sion!
Count
(ironically, to Figaro)
dun - que? Co - rag - gio!
well now? Speak free - ly!
Figaro (pretending to recollect)
O che te - sta! o che te - sta!
O how stu - pid, now I know it!
cresc.
f p
quest' è la pa - ten - te, che poc' an - zi il fan - ciul - lo mi
That is the com - mis - sion which the boy has en - trust - ed to

Count
Figaro (confused)
diè.
me.
Per chè fa - re?
For what rea - son?
Vi man - ca. . .
It need - ed. . .
Susanna (softly, to Figaro)
Il su - gel - lo.
need-ed seal-ing.
Countess (softly, to Susanna)
Il su - gel - lo.
need-ed seal-ing.
Count
Figaro
Vi man - ca?
It need - ed. . .
ri - spon - di!
I'm wait - ing. . .
È l'u -
It's the
(pretending to ponder)
Count
Figaro
san - za. . .
cus - tom –
Sù via, ti con - fon - di?
Well, what is the cus - tom?
È l'u - san - za di
It's the cus - tom to
cresc.
f

Susanna
(aside)
Count (Aside, notices that the seal is missing, tears up the paper and angrily throws it away.)
Se mi
If I
por - vi il su - gel - lo. Que - sto bir - bo mi to - glie il cer -
seal a com - mis - sion. Oh, that ras - cal is driv - ing me
p
sal - vo da que - sta tem - pe - - - -
ev - er es - cape from this ship - - - -
Countess (aside)
Se mi sal - vo da que - sta tem - pe - sta, più non
If I ev - er es - cape from this ship - wreck, nev - er -
Count
vel - lo, tut - to, tut - to è un mi -
cra - zy. This af - fair is a
Figaro (aside)
Sbuf - fa in - va - no, e la ter - ra cal - pe - sta! po - ve -
Let him threat - en as much as he pleas - es, he will

- - - sta, se mi sal - vo da
- - - wreck, if I ev - er es-
hav-vi nau-fra-gio per me, se mi sal - vo da
more will I ven-ture to sea, if I ev - er es-
ste - ro per me, que - sto bir - bo mi
mys - t'ry to me, oh, this ras - cal is
ri - no, ne sa men di me, sbuf - fa in - va - no e la
not get the bet-ter of me, let him threat - en as
f p
fp
que - sta tem - pe - sta, più non hav - vi nau - fra - gio per
cape from this ship - wreck, nev - er - more will I ven - ture to
que - sta tem - pe - sta, più non hav - vi nau - fra - gio per
cape from this ship - wreck, nev - er - more will I ven - ture to
to - glie il cer - vel - lo, tut - to, tut - to è un mi - ste - ro per
driv - ing me cra - zy, this af - fair is a mys - t'ry to
ter - ra cal - pe - sta, po - ve - ri - no, ne sa men di
much as he pleas - es, he will not get the bet - ter of
f p

me, no, più non hav - vi nau - fra - gio per me, no,
sea, no, nev - er - more will I ven - ture to sea, no,
me, no, più non hav - vi nau - fra - gio per me, no,
sea, no, nev - er - more will I ven - ture to sea, no,
me, sì, tut - to, tut - to è un mi - ste - ro per me, sì,
me, yes, this af - fair is a mys - t'ry to me, yes,
me, sì, po - ve - ri - no, ne sa men di me, sì,
me, no, he will not get the bet - ter of me, no,
più non hav - vi nau - fra - gio per me.
nev - er - more will I ven - ture to sea.
più non hav - vi nau - fra - gio per me.
nev - er - more will I ven - ture to sea.
tut - to, tut - to è un mi - ste - ro per me.
this af - fair is a mys - t'ry to me.
po - ve - ri - no, ne sa men di me.
he will not get the bet - ter of me.

(Enter Marcellina, Basilio, and Bartolo.)
Allegro assai
Marcellina
Voi, si - gnor, che giu - sto
Lord, our case de-mands a
Basilio
Voi, si - gnor, che giu - sto
Lord, our case de-mands a
Bartolo
Voi, si - gnor, che giu - sto
Lord, our case de-mands a
Allegro assai
f
sie-te, ci do - ve - te or a - scol-tar.
hear-ing, that is why we came to-day.
sie-te, ci do - ve - te or a - scol-tar.
hear-ing, that is why we came to-day.
Count (aside)
sie-te, ci do - ve - te or a - scol-tar. Son ve -
hear-ing, that is why we came to-day. They have
p

Susanna (aside)
Son ve - nu - ti a scon - cer - tar - mi, qual ri -
They have come to give us troub - le, we must
Countess (aside)
Son ve - nu - ti a scon - cer - tar - mi, qual ri - me - dio ri - tro -
They have come to give us troub - le, we must lead their plans a -
nu - ti a ven - di - car - mi, io mi
come here for re - tri - bu - tion, things be -
Figaro (aside)
Son ve - nu - ti a scon - cer -
They have come to give us
me - dio ri - tro - var, qual ri - me - dio ri - tro - var?
lead their plans a - stray, we must lead their plans a - stray.
var, qual ri - me - dio, qual ri - me - dio ri - tro - var?
stray, we must lead, we must lead their plans a - stray.
sen - to a con - so - lar.
gin now to go my way.
tar - mi, qual ri - me - dio ri - tro - var?
troub - le, we must lead their plans a - stray.
f

Figaro
Son tre sto - li - di, tre paz - zi, co - sa
Bent on as - i - nine ob - struc - tion, those three
p
f
mai ven - go - no a far, co - sa mai ven - go - no a far?
fools are here to - day, those three fools are here to - day.
p
cresc.
f
p
Count
Pian, pia - nin, sen - za schia - maz - zi, di - ca o -
Let's not make a rash de - duc - tion, first each
f
p
gnun quel che gli par, di - ca o - gnun quel che gli par.
one must have has say, first each one must have his say.
Marcellina
Un im -
This man
cresc.
p
3

pe - gno nu - zi - a - le ha co - stui con me con -
gave his sol - emn prom - ise that in time we would be
trat-to, e pre-ten-do ch'il con-trat-to de-va me-co ef-fet-tuar.
mar-ried, I in-sist up-on this bar-gain be-ing prompt-ly car-ried out!
Susanna
Co - me! co - me?
Bar - gain? bar - gain?
Countess
Co - me! co - me?
Bar - gain? bar - gain?
Figaro
Co - me! co - me?
Bar - gain? bar - gain?
Count
O - là! Si -
No more, let

len - zio, si - len - zio si - len - zio! io son
no - bod - y dare in - ter - rupt me, it is
Bartolo
quì per giu - di - car. Io da
I who judge this case. With this
lei scel - to av - vo - ca - to, ven - go a far le sue di -
la - dy's wish com - pli - ant I am here as her at -
fe - se, le le - git - ti - me pre - te - se, io vi ven - go a pa - le -
tor - ney, and I war - rant that my cli - ent has a strict - ly le - gal

Susanna
È un bir - ban - te, è un bir - ban - te!
He's a scoun-drel, he's a scoun-drel!
Countess
È un bir - ban - te, è un bir - ban - te!
He's a scoun-drel, he's a scoun-drel!
Figaro
sar. È un bir - ban - te, è un bir - ban - te!
case! He's a scoun-drel, he's a scoun-drel!
Count
O - là! si - len - zio, si - len - zio, si - len - zio! io son quì per
E - nough! Be si - lent! Let's hear Don Ba - si - lio; it is I who
giu - di - car.
judge this case.
Basilio
Io com' uomal mon-do co-gni-to,ven-go quì per te-sti - mo - nio del pro-mes-so ma - tri - mo - nio, con pre - stan - za di da -
I, as man of prime ce - leb-ri-ty,give my word and tes-ti - mon - ial that their plans were mat - ri - mon - ial, with a bo - nus in ad -

Susanna
Son tre mat-ti, son tre mat-ti, son tre mat-ti, son tre mat - ti!
Ev-'ry one of them is cra - zy, ev-'ry one of them is cra - zy!
Countess
Son tre mat-ti, son tre mat-ti, son tre mat-ti, son tre mat - ti!
Ev-'ry one of them is cra - zy, ev-'ry one of them is cra - zy!
Figaro
nar. Son tre mat - ti, son tre mat - ti!
vance. They are cra - zy, they are cra - zy!
Count
O - là! si - len - zio! lo ve - dre - mo, il con - trat - to
Hold on! Ac - cord - ing to prop - er pro - ceed - ing, we must first give the
leg - ge - re - mo, tut - to in or - din de - ve an -
con - tract a read - ing, we must fol - low the le - gal

Più allegro
Susanna
Son con - fu - sa, son stor - di - ta,
What a course e-vents have tak-en!
Countess
Son con - fu - sa, son stor - di - ta,
What a_ course e - vents have tak-en!
Figaro
dar.
course.
Son con - fu - so, son stor - di - to,
What a_ course e - vents have tak-en!
Più allegro
di - spe - ra - ta, sba - lor - di - ta;
We are beat - en, bad - ly shak-en!
di - spe - ra - ta, sba-lor - di - ta;
We are beat-en, bad-ly_ shak-en!
Marcellina
Che bel col - po! che bel ca - so!
What a per - fect case of trap-ping!
Basilio
Che bel col - po! che bel ca - so!
What a per - fect case of trap-ping!
Count and Bartolo
Che bel col - po! che bel ca - so!
What a per - fect case of trap-ping!
Figaro
di - spe - ra - to_ sba - lor - di - to;
We are beat-en,_ bad-ly_ shak-en!

cer-to un dia - vol dell' in - fer - no quì li ha
Sure-ly some in - fer - nal pow - er must have
È cre - sciu - to a tut - ti il na - so. Qual - che
This time we have caught them nap - ping. Some pro -
Cer - to un dia - vol
Sure - ly some in -
fat - ti ca - pi - tar, cer - to un dia - vol quì li ha fat - ti ca - pi -
brought them here to - day, sure - ly some in - fer - nal pow - er brought them
nu - me a noi pro - pi - zio quì ci ha
pi - tious, kind - ly pow - er must have
dell' in - fer - no quì li ha fat - ti ca - pi -
fer - nal pow - er must have brought them here to -

tar, ca - pi - tar, son con -
here just to - day! What a
tar, ca - pi - tar, son con -
here just to - day! What a
fat - ti ca - pi - tar, ca - pi - tar;
brought us here to - day, just to - day!
fat - ti ca - pi - tar, ca - pi - tar;
brought us here to - day, just to - day!
fat - ti ca - pi - tar, ca - pi - tar;
brought them us here to - day, just to - day!
tar, ca - pi - tar; son con -
day, just to - day! What a
fu - sa, son stor - di - ta,
course e - vents have tak - en!
fu - sa, son stor - di - ta,
course e - vents have tak - en!
che bel col - po, che bel ca - so!
What a per - fect case of trap - ping!
che bel col - po, che bel ca - so!
What a per - fect case of trap - ping!
che bel col - po, che bel ca - so!
What a per - fect case of trap - ping!
fu - so, son stor - di - to,
course e - vents have tak - en!

di - spe - ra - ta, sba - lor - di - ta;
We are beat - en, bad - ly shak - en!
di - spe - ra - ta, sba - lor - di - ta;
We are beat - en, bad - ly shak - en!
è cre - sciu - to a tut - ti il
This time we have caught them
è cre - sciu - to a tut - ti il
This time we have caught them
è cre - sciu - to a tut - ti il
This time we have caught them
di - spe - ra - to, sba - lor - di - to;
We are beat - en, bad - ly shak - en!
cer - to un dia - vol_ dell' in - fer - no qui li ha fat - ti_ ca - pi -
Sure - ly some in - fer - nal pow - er must have brought them here to -
cer - to un dia - vol_ dell' in - fer - no qui li ha fat - ti_ ca - pi -
Sure - ly some in - fer - nal pow - er must have brought them here to -
na - so; è cre -
nap - ping. Yes, this
na - so; è cre -
nap - ping. Yes, this
na - so; è cre -
nap - ping. Yes, this
cer - to un dia - vol quì li ha
Some in - fer - nal pow - er

tar, quì li ha fat - ti ca - pi - tar.
day, must have brought them here to - day.
tar, quì li ha fat - ti ca - pi - tar.
day, must have brought them here to - day.
sciu - to a tut - ti il na - so.
time we caught them nap - ping.
sciu - to a tut - ti il na - so.
time we caught them nap - ping.
sciu - to a tut - ti il na - so.
time we caught them nap - ping.
fat - ti ca - pi - tar.
brought them here to - day.
Son con - fu - sa,
With their le - gal
sotto voce
Son con -
With their
sotto voce
Qual - che nu - me
Some pro - pi - tious
sotto voce
Qual - che nu - me
Some pro - pi - tious
sotto voce
Qual - che nu - me
Some pro - pi - tious
sotto voce
Son con -
With their
p

son stor - di - ta, di - spe -
ma - chi - na - tions, they have
fu - sa, son stor - di - ta,
le - gal ma - chi - na - tions,
a noi pro - pi - zio
and kind - ly pow - er
a noi pro - pi - zio
and kind - ly pow - er
a noi pro - pi - zio
and kind - ly pow - er
fu - so, son stor - di - to,
le - gal ma - chi - na - tions,
ra - ta, sba - lor - di - ta; cer - to un
caused new com - pli - ca - tions. Some in -
di - spe - ra - ta, sba - lor - di - ta; cer - to un
they have caused new com - pli - ca - tions. Some in -
quì ci ha fat - ti
must have brought us
quì ci ha fat - ti
must have brought us
quì li ci ha fat - ti
must have brought them us
di - spe - ra - to, sba - lor - di - to; cer - to un
they have caused new com - pli - ca - tions. Some in -
f
p
f

dia - vol dell' in - fer - no quì li ha fat - ti, quì li ha
fer - nal e - vil pow - er, some in - fer - nal pow - er
dia - vol dell' in - fer - no quì li ha fat - ti, quì li ha
fer - nal e - vil pow - er, some in - fer - nal pow - er
ca - pi - tar, quì ci ha fat - ti, ci ha fat - ti
here to - day, must have brought, must have brought us
ca - pi - tar, quì ci ha fat - ti, ci ha fat - ti
here to - day, must have brought, must have brought us
ca - pi - tar, quì [li ci] ha fat - ti, [li ci] ha fat - ti
here to - day, must have brought, must have brought [them us]
dia - vol dell' in - fer - no quì li ha fat - ti, quì li ha
fer - nal e - vil pow - er, some in - fer - nal pow - er
fat - ti ca - pi - tar. Son con - fu - sa, son stor - di -
brought them here to - day! What a course e - vents have tak -
fat - ti ca - pi - tar. Son con - fu - sa, son stor -
brought them here to - day! What a course e - vents have
ca - pi - tar.
here to - day!
ca - pi - tar.
here to - day!
ca - pi - tar.
here to - day!
fat - ti ca - pi - tar. Son con - fu - so, son stor -
brought them here to - day! What a course e - vents have

- ta, di - spe-ra - ta, sba-lor-di - ta, son
- en, we are beat - en, bad-ly shak - en. With
di - ta, di - spe-ra - ta, sba-lor-di-ta;
tak - en, we are beat - en, bad-ly shak-en.
p
Che bel
What a
p
Che bel
What a
p
Che bel
What a
di - to, di - spe - ra - to, sba-lor-di-to;
tak - en, we are beat - en, bad-ly shak-en.
con-fu - sa, son stor-di - ta, di -
their le - gal ma - chi-na - tions they
son con - fu - sa,
They have caused new
col-po! che bel ca-so! è cre-sciu-to a tut-ti il na-so,
per-fect case of trap-ping, this time we have caught them nap-ping,
col-po! che bel ca-so! è cre-sciu-to a tut-ti il na-so,
per-fect case of trap-ping, this time we have caught them nap-ping,
col-po! che bel ca-so! è cre-sciu-to a tut-ti il na-so,
per-fect case of trap-ping, this time we have caught them nap-ping,
son con - fu - so,
They have caused new

sf p f
- - spe - ra - ta, sba - lor - di - - ta. Cer - to un
— have caused — new com - pli - ca - tions. Sure - ly
sf p f
sba - lor - di - ta. Cer - to un
com - pli - ca - tions. Sure - ly
sf p
è cre - sciu - to a tut - ti il na - so.
this time we have caught them nap - ping.
sf p
è cre - sciu - to a tut - ti il na - so.
this time we — have caught them nap - ping.
sf p
è cre - sciu - to a tut - ti il na - so.
this time we have caught them nap - ping.
sf p
sba - lor - di - to;
com - pli - ca - tions.
sf p f
Susanna and the Countess
dia - vol - dell' in - fer - no qui li ha fat - ti ca - pi - tar, ca - pi -
some in - fer - nal pow - er must have brought them here to - day, just to -
Marcellina
f
Qual - che nu - me a noi — pro - pi - zio
Some — pro - pi - tious and kind - ly pow - er
Basilio
f
Qual - che nu - me a noi — pro - pi - zio
Some — pro - pi - tious and kind - ly pow - er
Count
f
Qual - che nu - me a noi — pro - pi - zio
Some — pro - pi - tious and kind - ly pow - er
Bartolo
f
Qual - che nu - me
Some pro - pi - tious
Figaro
f
cer - to un dia - vol dell' in - fer - no
Sure - ly some in - fer - nal pow - er

tar, qui liha fat - ti ca - pi - tar, cer - to un
day, must have brought them here to - day, sure - ly
quì ci ha fat - ti, ci ha fat - ti ca - pi - tar,
must have brought us to them this ver - y day.
quì ci ha fat - ti, ci ha fat - ti ca - pi - tar,
must have brought us to them this ver - y day.
quì li ha fat - ti ca - pi - tar,
must have brought them here to - day.
quì ci ha fat - ti ca - pi - tar,
pow - er brought us here to - day.
quì li ha fat - ti ca - pi - tar,
brought them here this ver - y day.
dia - vol dell' in - fer - no quì li ha fat - ti ca - pi - tar, ca - pi -
some in - fer - nal pow - er must have brought them here to - day, just to -
qual - che nu - me a noi pro - pi - zio
Some pro - pi - tious and kind - ly pow - er
qual - che nu - me a noi pro - pi - zio
Some pro - pi - tious and kind - ly pow - er
qual - che nu - me a noi pro - pi - zio
Some pro - pi - tious and kind - ly pow - er
qual - che nu - me
Some pro - pi - tious
cer - to un dia - vol dell' in - fer - no
Sure - ly some in - fer - nal pow - er

tar, quì li ha fat - ti ca - pi -
day, must have brought them here to -
quì ci ha fat - ti, ci ha fat - ti ca - pi -
must have brought, must have brought us here to -
quì ci ha fat - ti, ci ha fat - ti ca - pi -
must have brought, must have brought us here to -
quì li ha fat - ti ca - pi -
must have brought them here to -
quì ci ha fat - ti ca - pi -
pow - er brought us here to -
quì li ha fat - ti ca - pi -
brought them here this ver - y
Susanna
tar. Cer -
day! Sure -
Countess
tar.
day!
Marcellina
p
tar. Che bel col - po! che bel ca - so!
day! What a per - fect case of trap-ping,
Basilio
p
tar. Che bel col - po! che bel ca - so!
day! What a per - fect case of trap-ping,
Count and Bartolo
p
tar. Che bel col - po! che bel ca - so!
day! What a per - fect case of trap-ping,
sotto voce
tar. Son con -
day! With their
p

- to un dia - vol dell' in - fer - no qui li ha
- ly some in - fer - nal pow - er must have
sotto voce
Son con - fu - sa, son stor - di - ta, di - spe -
With their le - gal ma - chi - na - tions, they have
è cre-sciu - to a tut - ti il na - so, qual - che
this time we have caught them nap-ping. Some pro -
è cre-sciu - to a tut - ti il na - so, qual - che
this time we have caught them nap-ping. Some pro -
è cre-sciu - to a tut - ti il na - so, qual - che
this time we have caught them nap-ping. Some pro -
fu - so, son stor - di - to, di - spe - ra - to,
le - gal ma - chi - na - tions, they have caused us
fat - ti ca - pi - tar, ca - pi -
brought them here to - day, them here to -
ra - ta, sba - lor - di - ta;
caused us com - pli - ca - tions.
nu - me a noi pro - pi - zio, quì ci ha fat - ti ca - pi -
pi - tious kind - ly pow - er must have brought us here to -
nu - me a noi pro - pi - zio, quì ci ha fat - ti ca - pi -
pi - tious kind - ly pow - er must have brought us here to -
nu - me a noi pro - pi - zio, quì [li ci] ha fat - ti ca - pi -
pi - tious kind - ly pow - er must have brought [them us] here to -
sba - lor - di - to;
com - pli - ca - tions.

f
tar; cer - to un dia - vol dell' in -
day. Sure - ly some in - fer - nal
f
cer - to un dia - vol dell' in - fer - no
Sure - ly some in - fer - nal pow - er
f
tar; qual - che nu - me a noi pro -
day. Some pro - pi - tious kind - ly
f
tar; qual - che nu - me a noi pro -
day. Some pro - pi - tious kind - ly
f
tar; qual - che nu - me a noi pro -
day. Some pro - pi - tious kind - ly
f
cer - to un dia - vol dell' in - fer - no
Sure - ly some in - fer - nal pow - er
f
fer - no quì li ha fat - ti ca - pi -
pow - er must have brought them here to -
quì li ha fat - ti, li ha fat - ti ca - pi -
must have brought them to us this ver - y
pi - zio quì ci ha fat - ti ca - pi -
pow - er must have brought us here to -
pi - zio quì ci ha fat - ti ca - pi -
pow - er must have brought us here to -
pi - zio quì li ci ha fat - ti ca - pi -
pow - er must have brought them us here to -
quì li ha fat - ti, li ha fat - ti ca - pi -
must have brought them to us this ver - y

tar, cer - to un dia - vol dell' in -
day. Sure - ly some in - fer - nal
tar, cer - to un dia - vol dell' in - fer - no
day. Sure - ly some in - fer - nal pow - er
tar. Qual - che nu - me a noi pro -
day. Some pro - pi - tious kind - ly
tar. Qual - che nu - me a noi pro
day. Some pro - pi - tious kind - ly
tar. Qual - che nu - me a noi pro -
day. Some pro - pi - tious and kind - ly
tar. Cer - to un dia - vol dell' in - fer - no
day. Some in - fer - nal e - vil pow - er
fer - no quì li ha fat - ti ca - pi - tar,
pow - er must have brought them here to - day.
quì li ha fat - ti, li ha fat - ti ca - pi - tar,
must have brought them to us this ver - y day.
pi - zio quì ci ha fat - ti ca - pi - tar,
pow - er brought us here this ver - y day.
pi - zio quì ci ha fat - ti ca - pi - tar,
pow - er brought us here this ver - y day.
pi - zio quì li ci ha fat - ti ca - pi - tar,
pow - er. brought them us here this ver - y day.
quì li ha fat - ti, li ha fat - ti ca - pi - tar,
must have brought them to us this ver - y day.

Prestissimo
cer - to un dia - vol dell' in - fer - no
Sure - ly some in - fer - nal pow - er
qual - che
Some pro -
Prestissimo
sf
p
cresc.
f
quì li ha fat - ti ca - pi - tar. Cer - to un
brought them here this ver - y day. Sure - ly
nu - me quì ci ha fat - ti ca - pi - tar.
pi - tious pow - er brought us here to - day.
nu - me quì li ci ha fat - ti ca - pi - tar.
pi - tious pow - er brought them us here to - day.
42226

dia - vol dell' in - fer - no quì li ha
some in - fer - nal pow - er brought them
dia - vol dell' in - fer - no quì li ha
some in - fer - nal pow - er brought them
Qual - che nu - me quì ci ha
Some pro - pi - tious pow - er
Qual - che nu - me quì ci ha
Some pro - pi - tious pow - er
Qual - che nu - me quì li ci ha
Some pro - pi - tious pow - er
dia - vol dell' in - fer - no quì li ha
some in - fer - nal pow - er brought them
cresc.
f
fat - ti ca - pi - tar, ca - pi - tar,
here this ver - y day, brought them here,
fat - ti ca - pi - tar, ca - pi - tar,
here this ver - y day, brought them here,
fat - ti ca - pi - tar, ca - pi - tar,
brought us here to - day, brougnt us here,
fat - ti ca - pi - tar, ca - pi - tar,
brought us here to - day, brought us here,
fat - ti ca - pi - tar, ca - pi - tar,
brought them us here to - day, brought them us here,
fat - ti ca - pi - tar, ca - pi - tar,
here this ver - y day, brought them here,

ca - pi - tar, ca - pi - tar.
on this day, on this day.
ca - pi - tar, ca - pi - tar.
on this day, on this day.
ca - pi - tar, ca - pi - tar.
on this day, on this day.
ca - pi - tar, ca - pi - tar.
on this day, on this day.
ca - pi - tar, ca - pi - tar.
on this day, on this day.
ca - pi - tar, ca - pi - tar.
on this day, on this day.

End of Act II

Act III

(Scene: *A richly decorated hall prepared for a wedding festivity, with two thrones.)*

Recitative

Count, Countess, and Susanna

for- se qual-cun de'miei vas-sal- li. . . a si-mil raz-za è com-mu-me l'ar-
been e-ven one of the do-mes-tics, they are the kind who would take such a
dir, ma la Con-tes-sa— ah, che un dub-bio l'of-fen-de! el-la ri-
chance. As for the Count-ess— an-y doubt would be in-sult; she has too
spet-ta trop-po se stes-sa, e l'o-nor mi-o, l'o-
much re-spect for her-self and for my hon-or. My
no-re. . . do-ve, dia-min, l'ha po-sto u-ma-no er-ro-re!
hon-or! What has hu-man weak-ness done to my hon-or!
Countess (entering with Susanna, and keeping in the background, unseen by the Count) Count
Via! fat-ti co-re, di-gli che ti at-ten-da in giar-di-no. Sa-
Come! don't be down-cast. Tell him he may meet you in the gar-den. I'll make

prò, se Che-ru-bi-no e-ra giun-to a Si - vi - glia, a ta-le og-get-to ho man-da - to Ba-
sure that Che-ru-bi - no ar-rived at Se-ville. I've sent Ba - si - lio ex-press-ly for that
Susanna
Countess
si - lio. O cie - lo! e Fi - ga - ro? A lui non dei dir
pur - pose. Good Heav - ens, and Fi - ga - ro? He must not know a -
Count
nul - la, in - ve - ce tu - a, vo-glio an - dar - ci io me - des - ma. A - van - ti se - ra
bout it— in-stead of you,— I'll a - wait him my-self. Be-fore this eve-ning
Susanna
Countess
do - vreb - be ri - tor - nar. O Di - o! non o - so! Pen - sa
he ought to be back. My la - dy, I'm fright-ened! Re-mem - ber
(She retires.)
Count
ch'è in tua ma - no il mio ri - po - so. E Su - san - na? Chi sà, ch'el - la tra-
that my fate is in your hands now. And Su - san - na? Who knows, may - be she
di - to ab - bia il se - gre - to mi - o, oh, se ha par - la - to, gli
has al - read - y be-trayed my se - cret. If she has done so, Fi - ga - ro must

Susanna
Count (gravely)
fo spo - sar la vec - chia. (Marcel - li - na!) Si - gnor! Co - sa bra -
mar - ry Mar - cel - li - na. (Mar - cel - li - na!) My lord! What do you
Susanna
Count
ma - te? Mi par che sie - te in col - le - ra! Vo - le - te qual - che
wish? You seem in bad hu - mor. What is it that you
Susanna
co - sa? Si - gnor, la vo - stra spo - sa hai so - li - ti va -
want? My lord, just now the Count - ess is suf - f'ring from a
Count
po - ri, e vi chie - de il va - set - to de - gli o - do - ri. Pren -
head - ache and sent me to get your flask of smell - ing salts.
Susanna
Count
de - te. Or vel ri - por - to. Ah no; po - te - te ri - te - ner - lo per
Take it. I'll soon re - turn it. No, no, don't both - er, you may need it your -
Susanna
Count
voi. Per me? que - sti non son ma - li da don - ne tri - via - li. Un' a -
self. My - self? Peo - ple of my kind do not suf - fer from head - aches. But a

Susanna
man - te che per - de il ca - ro spo - so sul pun-to d'ot-te-ner - lo. Pa -
bride a - bout to lose her bride-groom on the day of her wed-ding? I'll
gan - do Mar - cel - li - na col - la do - te che voi mi pro-met -
pay off Mar - cel - li - na with the dow - ry that you prom - ised to
Count
Susanna
te - ste. Ch'io vi pro - mi - si! quan - do? Cre - dea d'a - ver-lo in -
give me. I made that prom - ise? Did I? That's how I un - der -
Count
Susanna
te - so. Sì, se vo - lu - to a - ve-ste in - ten - der-mi voi stes - sa. È mio do -
stood you. Yes, yes, if you had on - ly wished to un-der-stand me. It is my
ve - re, e quel di sua Ec - cel - len - za è il mio vo - le - re.
du - ty, and what your lord - ship wish - es is my de - sire.

No. 16. Crudel! perchè finora

But why, why make me suffer

Duetto

Count and Susanna

No, non vi man - che-
No, no, you have my
Count
E non mi man - che-ra-i?
You will not fail to be there?
rò, sì! no!
word. Yes! no!
Ver - ra - i? non man-che - ra - i, non man-che -
You prom - ise? won't dis-ap-point me? this ver - y
fp
fp
fp
non man - che - rò, no, non vi man-che - rò.
You have my word, I will not fail my word.
ra - i?
eve-ning?
Mi
The

sen - to dal con - ten - to pie - no di gio - ia il
sweet prom - ise you gave me rais - es my hope so
fp
cresc.
p
(aside)
Scu-sa - te-mi se men - to! voi che in-ten-de-te a - mor, scu-sa - te-mi,
All those who know what love is, forgive me for this lie, all those who know
cor, mi sen - to dal con - ten - to
high, the sweet prom - ise you gave me
voi che in-ten-de-te a - mor.
love will for-give this lie.
pie - no di gio - ia il cor. Dun-que in giar-din ver - ra - i?
rais - es my hope so high. You'll meet me in the gar-den?

Se piace a voi, verrò.
If that's your wish, I might.
No, non vi manche-
I shall be there to-
E non mi man-che-ra - i?
You will not dis-ap-point me?
rò.
night.
Sì!
Yes!
no!
no!
dolce
Ver-ra - i?
You prom - ise?
non man-che-ra - i?
won't dis-ap-point me?
dun-que ver-ra - i?
I have your prom - ise?
no! sì, se_pia-ce a voi ver-rò,
no! yes, I_ shall be_ there to-night.
dolce
no?
no?
non man-che-ra - i?
Won't dis-ap-point me?
f
p

no!
sì!
sì!
no,
no, non vi
no!
yes!
yes!
no,
I shall be
dun-que ver-ra - i?
non man-che-ra - i?
sì?
and you will be there?
won't dis-ap-point me?
yes?
f
p
man - che - rò.
Scu-sa - te-mi se - men-to,
there to - night.
All those who know what love is,
(with joy)
Mi sen-to dal con - ten - to
pie-no di gio-ia il
The sweet prom - ise you gave me
rais-es my hope so
sf
p
cresc.
p
voi che in-ten-de - te a - mor,
scu-sa - te-mi se
men-to, scu-sa - te-mi,
they will for-give this lie,
all those who know what love is,
all those who know
cor,
mi sen-to
dal con - ten - to
high,
the sweet prom - ise
you gave me
sfp
sfp
sfp

voi che in-ten-de - te a - mor, voi che in-ten-de - te a - mor,
love will for-give this lie, they will for-give this lie,
pie - no di gio - ia il cor, pie - no di gio - ia il cor,
rais - es my hope so high, rais - es my hope so high,
voi che in-ten-de - te a - mor, voi che in - ten-de - te a - mor, voi
they will for-give this lie, they will for-give this lie, they
pie - no di gio - ia il cor, pie - no di gio - ia il cor, pie -
rais - es my hope so high, my hope so high, my
che in - ten-de - te a - mor
will for-give this lie.
no di gio - ia il cor.
hope so high.
cresc.

Recitative

Count, Susanna, and Figaro

Susanna
mi - o. . . ma la Con-tes - sa at - ten-de-rà il va-set - to. Eh fu un pre-
point me? But the Count-ess! she is wait-ing for her smelling salts. She real-ly
Count
te - sto, par - la - to io non a - vrei sen - za di que - sto. Ca -
is - n't, I had to make some pre - text to ad - dress you. A -
(taking her hand)
Susanna (drawing it away)
Count
Susanna
ris - si - ma! Vien gen - te. (È mia senz' al - tro.) For - bi - te - vi la
dor - a - ble! They're com - ing! (She has sur - ren - dered.) Don't count your
Figaro (Enters,[aside, to Susanna])
Susanna (aside, to Figaro)
boc - ca, o si - gnor scal - tro. Ehi! Su - san - na, o - ve và - i? Ta - ci.
chick - ens be - fore they're hatched. Say, Su - san - na, what's up? Plen - ty!
(Exit Susanna,)
Figaro (Follows her.)
Sen-za av - vo - ca - to hai già vin - ta la cau - sa. Cos' è na - to?
With-out a law - yer, you have won the de - ci - sion. What has hap - pened?

No.17. Hai già vinta la causa!...Vedrò mentr'io sospiro

You have won the decision? ...Shall I look on desiring

Recitative and Aria

Count

a pia-cer mi - o la sen-ten - za sa - rà.
I'll base my ver-dict on my plea - sure a - lone.
Andante
p
Ma s'ei pa - gas-se la vec-chia pre-ten - den - te?
If he suc - ceed-ed in pay-ing Mar-cel - li - na!
Tempo I°
p
Pa-gar-la!
How can he?
In qual ma-nie - ra!
He has no mon-ey!
f
E poi v'è An - to - nio che all'in - co - gni - to Fi - ga - ro ri - cu - sa di
Be - sides, An - to - nio won't per - mit his be-lov - ed niece Su - san - na to
p

da-re u-na ni-po-te in ma-tri-mo-nio.
mar-ry such a no-bod-y as Fi-ga-ro.
Col-ti-van-do l'or-go-glio di que-sto men-te-cat-to. . .
I will flat-ter the e-go of that con-ceit-ed drunkard.
cresc.
Tut-to gio-va a un rag-gi-ro. . .
It will fur-ther my pur-pose.
il col-po è fat-to.
It can't go bet-ter!
cresc.

Allegro maestoso
Ve -
Shall
p
tr
drò men-tr' io so - spi - ro, fe - li - ce un ser - vo
I look on de - sir - ing, and see my ser - vant
cresc.
mi - o!
hap-py?
E un
Shall
f
p
tr
ben che in-van de - si - o, ei pos - se-der do - vrà? Ve -
I see him ac - quir - ing fa - vors for which I yearn? Shall
tr
tr
cresc.
f
sfp
p

drò per man d'a - mo - re u - ni - ta a un vi - le og - get - to chi in
I, in help - less fash - ion, al - low a hate - ful mar - riage, while
tr
me de - stò un af - fet - to, che per me poi non ha, che
I re - strain a pas - sion which she does not re - turn, which
per me poi non ha. Ve - drò men - tr' io so - spi - ro, fe -
she does not re - turn? Shall I look on de - sir - ing, and
f
p
cresc.
fp
li - ce un ser - vo mi - o, ve - drò che un ben ch'io de - si - o, ei
see my ser - vant hap - py? Shall I see him ac - quir - ing the
sf
3

pos - se - der do - vrà? Ve - drò per man d'a - mo - re u -
prize for which I yearn? Shall I not lift a fin - ger to
ni - ta a un vi - le og - get - to, chi in me de - stò un af - fet - to, che
con - quer her af - fec - tion, look on with - out ob - jec - tion, a -
tr
per me poi non ha, che per me poi non ha, ve -
loof and un - con - cerned, a - loof and un - con - cerned? Ah,
3
drò? ve - drò? ve - drò? ve - drò? Ah
no! I won't! Ah, no! I won't! Ah,
cresc.
f
3

Allegro assai
no! la-sciar - ti in pa - ce non vo' que-sto con - ten - to,
no, I will not give you so great a sat - is - fac - tion;
p
f
tu non na - sce - sti, au - da - ce, tu non na - sce - sti, au - da - ce, per
you shall not dare to spite me, you shall not dare to spite me, op -
da - re a me tor - men - to, e for - se an - cor per
pose me and tor - ment me; you'll have no chance to
ri - de - re, per ri - de - re di mia in - fe - li - ci -
laugh at me, to laugh at me, while I am cast a -
sf

tà. Già la spe-ran-za so-la del-le ven-det-te
side. On-ly the thought of ven-geance of-fers me con-so-
mi-e quest' a-ni-ma con-so-la, e giu-bi-lar mi
la-tion; tri-um-phant vin-di-ca-tion shall sat-is-fy my
cresc.
fa, e giu-bi-lar, e giu-bi-lar mi fa. Ah, che la-sciar-ti in
pride, my wounded pride, my deep-ly wound-ed pride. Ah, I will nev-er
p f p f p
pa-ce non vo' que-sto con-ten-to, tu non na-sce-sti, au-
give you so great a sat-is-fac-tion; you shall not dare to
f p

da - ce, per da - re a me tor - men-to, e for - se an-cor per
spite me, op - pose me and tor - ment me, you'll have no chance to
f
p
ri - de-re, per ri - de-re di mia in - fe - li - ci - tà.
laugh at me, to laugh at me, while I ___ am cast a - side.
sf
sf p
tr
Già la spe - ran - za so - la del - le ven - det - te mi - e quest'
On - ly the thought of ven-geance of - fers me con - so - la - tion; tri -
cresc.
a - ni - ma con - so - la, e giu - bi - lar mi fa, e giu - bi -
um - phant vin - di - ca - tion shall sat - is - fy my pride, my wound-ed
f
p

lar, e giu - bi - lar mi fa, e giu - bi - lar,
pride, and fill my heart with joy, my heart with joy,
f
p
tr
e giu - bi - lar
and fill my heart
tr
mi fa, e giu - bi - lar mi fa, e
with joy, and fill my heart with joy, and
cresc.
(Prepares to leave, but meets Don Curzio, who enters with Mar-
giu - bi - lar mi fa.
fill my heart with joy.
tr
tr
f
cellina, Figaro, and Bartolo.)
tr

Recitative

Don Curzio, Marcellina, Figaro, Count, and Bartolo

Bartolo
Figaro
tà di sua Ec-cel-len-za. Che su-per-ba sen-ten-za! In che su-per-ba?
flat-ter me, your lord-ship. What a glo-ri-ous sen-tence! In what way glo-rious?
Bartolo
Figaro
Bartolo
Siam tut-ti ven-di-ca-ti. Io non la spo-se-rò. La spo-se-
Full jus-tice has been ren-dered. But I will not give in. Oh, yes, you
Curzio
ra-i. O pa-gar-la,o spo-sar-la, lei t'ha pre-sta-ti due mil-le pez-zi
will! Ei-ther marry or pay her. Did she not lend you two thou-sand sil-ver
Figaro
du-ri. Son gen-til-uo-mo, e sen-za l'as-sen-so de' miei no-bi-li pa-
piec-es? I am a no-ble-man, and can-not be mar-ried with-out my par-ents' con-
Count
Figaro
ren-ti... Do-ve so-no? chi so-no? La-scia-te an-cor cer-
sent! And these par-ents, where are they? I still am on the

Bartolo
car - li; do - po die - ci an - ni io spe - ro di tro - var - li. Qual - che bam -
look - out. In a - bout ten years I am sure I will have found them. So you
Figaro
Count
bin tro - va - to? No, per - du - to, dot - tor, an - zi ru - ba - to. Co - me?
are a found - ling? No, a "lost - ling," it seems that I was kid - napped. Kid - napped?
Marcellina
Bartolo
Don Curzio
Figaro
Co - sa? La pro - va? Il te - sti - mo - nio? L'o - ro, le gem - me, e i
Kid - napped? Then prove it! Where is your ev - i - dence? That I can of - fer! The
ri - ca - ma - ti pan - ni, che ne' più te - ne - ri an - ni mi ri - tro - va - ro a -
gold and pre - cious jew - els that my ab - duc - tors found near me, the fine em - broid - ered
dos - so i ma - sna - die - ri, so - no gl'in - di - zi ve - ri di mia na - sci - tà il -
lin - en I was wear - ing are the con - fir - ma - tion of my no - ble ex -

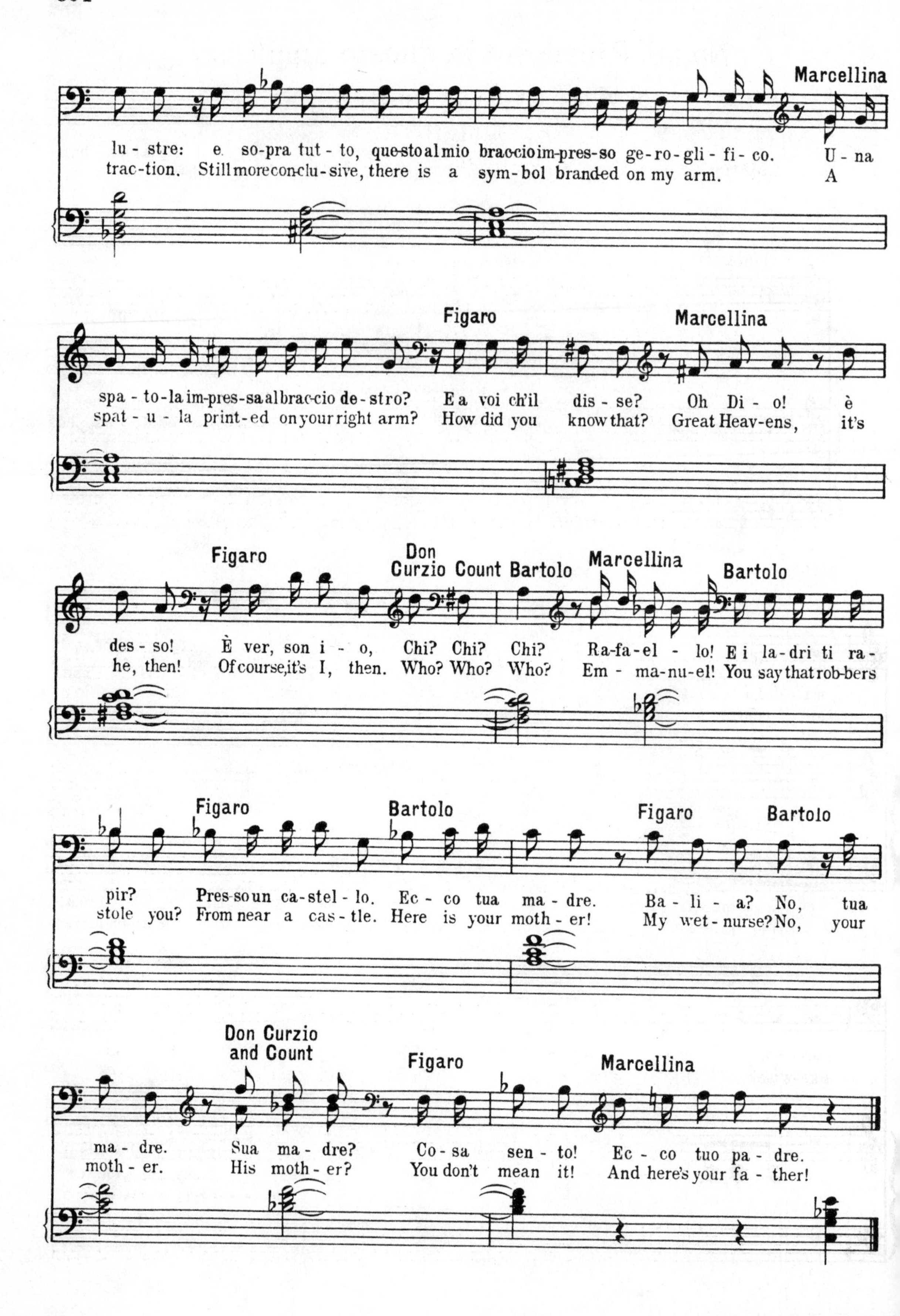
Marcellina
lu - stre: e so-pra tut - to, questo al mio braccio im-pres-so ge-ro-gli - fi - co. U - na
trac-tion. Still more con-clu-sive, there is a sym-bol branded on my arm. A
Figaro
Marcellina
spa - to - la im-pres-sa al braccio de - stro? E a voi ch'il dis - se? Oh Di - o! è
spat - u - la print-ed on your right arm? How did you know that? Great Heav-ens, it's
Figaro
Don Curzio
Count
Bartolo
Marcellina
Bartolo
des - so! È ver, son i - o, Chi? Chi? Chi? Ra-fa-el - lo! E i la-dri ti ra-
he, then! Of course, it's I, then. Who? Who? Who? Em - ma-nu-el! You say that rob-bers
Figaro
Bartolo
Figaro
Bartolo
pir? Pres-so un ca-stel - lo. Ec - co tua ma - dre. Ba - li - a? No, tua
stole you? From near a cas - tle. Here is your moth - er! My wet - nurse? No, your
Don Curzio and Count
Figaro
Marcellina
ma - dre. Sua ma - dre? Co - sa sen - to! Ec - co tuo pa - dre.
moth - er. His moth - er? You don't mean it! And here's your fa - ther!

No. 18. Riconosci in questo amplesso

Now at last I may embrace you

Sestetto

Marcellina, Figaro, Bartolo, Don Curzio, Count, and Susanna

ster - za la co - scien - za far non la - scia al tuo de -
du - ty to in - form you of the jus - tice of your
Don Curzio
Ei suo pa-dre, el - la sua ma - dre! l'i - me -
He the fa-ther, and she his moth-er! Then this
Count
sir.
claim.
Son smar-ri - to, son stor-di - to,
Worse mis-for-tune could not hap-pen!
Marcellina
Fi - glio a - ma - to!
I'm your moth - er!
neo non può se - guir, ei suo pa - dre, el - la sua
match is null and void; he the fa - ther and she the
Bartolo
Me-glio è as-sai di quà par - tir.
All my hopes have been de - stroyed.
Fi - glio a -
I'm your

Marcellina
Fi - glio a - ma - to!
He's your fa - ther!
Don Curzio
ma - dre!
moth - er!
l'i - me - neo non può se -
Then this match is null and
Count
Son smar-ri - to, son stor - di - to,
Worse mis-for-tune could not hap - pen!
Bartolo
ma - to!
fa - ther!
Fi - glio a -
She's your
Figaro
Pa - ren - ti a - ma - ti!
Be - lov - ed par-ents!
(Enter Susanna with a purse in her hand.)
Fi - glio a - ma - to!
I'm your moth-er!
guir, no,
void, yes,
l'i - me - neo non può se - guir.
then this match is null and void.
(about to go)
me - glio è as - sai di quà par - tir, di quà par - tir.
All my hopes have been de - stroyed, they are de - stroyed!
ma - to!
moth - er!
Fi - glio a - ma - to!
I'm your fa - ther!
Pa - ren - ti a - ma - ti! Pa - ren - ti a - ma - ti!
Be - lov - ed par-ents, be - lov - ed par - ents!
cresc.
tr
f

Susanna (detaining the Count)
Al-to, al-to! si-gnor Con-te, mil-le dop-pie son qui
Wait a mo-ment, not so hast-y. I have brought a-long the
p
pron-te, a pa-gar ven-go per Fi-ga-ro, ed a por-lo in li-ber-
mon-ey. It's the ran-som for my Fi-ga-ro, so that I can buy him
Marcellina
tà. Fi-glio a-ma-to!
free. Come, em-brace me!
Don Curzio
Non sap-piam com' è la co-sa,
There has been a great sen-sa-tion!
Count
Non sap-piam com' è la co-sa, com' è la co-sa, os-ser-
There has been a great sen-sa-tion, a great sen-sa-tion, take a
Bartolo
Fi-glio a-ma-to! Fi-glio a-
Come, em-brace me! Come, em-
Figaro
Pa-ren-ti a-ma-ti!
I love you dear-ly!

fi - glio a - ma - to! fi - glio a -
Let me kiss you! Let me
os - ser - va - te un po - co là, os - ser - va - te un po - co
Take a look and you will see, take a look and you will
va - te un po - co là, un po - co là, os - ser - va - te un po - co
look and you will see, and you will see, take a look and you will
ma - to! fi - glio a -
brace me! Come, em -
pa - ren - ti a - ma - ti! pa - ren - ti a -
I love you dear - ly, I love you
cresc.
ma - to!
kiss you!
Susanna (Turns and sees Figaro embracing Marcellina.)
là. Già d'ac-cor-do col-la spo-sa? Giu - sti Dei, che in-fe - del-
see! So he mar-ries Mar-cel - li - na! Lord in Heav'n, to be so
là.
see!
ma - to!
brace me!
ma - ti!
dear - ly!
f p
fp fp fp fp

(about to go)
tà, che in-fe - del - tà!
false, so false to me!
La-scia, i - ni - quo!
Don't come near me!
Figaro
(detaining Susanna)
No, t'ar-
Wait a
cresc.
f
p
La - scia, i - ni - quo!
Don't come near me!
re - sta!
mo - ment!
No, t'ar - re - sta!
You're mis - tak - en!
(Tears herself away and boxes Figaro's ears.)
Sen - ti
I am
Sen - ti, o ca - ra, sen - ti, sen - ti!
Lis - ten, my dar - ling, lis - ten, lis - ten!

que - sta!
lis - t'ning!
Marcellina
È un ef - fet - to
This pe - cu - liar
Count
Fre - mo, sma-nio dal fu -
I'm be-side my-self with
Bartolo
È un ef - fet - to
This pe - cu - liar
Figaro
È un ef - fet - to
This pe - cu - liar
Fre - mo, sma - nio dal fu - ro - re,
I'm be - side my - self with fu - ry,
di buon co - re,
fit of fu - ry
Don Curzio
Frè - me e sma - nia,
An - ger and quar - rels,
Count
ro - re, il de - sti - no me la
fu - ry, things have not turned out my
di buon co - re,
fit of fu - ry
di buon co - re,
fit of fu - ry

fre - mo, sma - nio dal fu - ro - re, fre - mo, sma - nio dal fu -
I'm be - side my - self with fu - ry, I'm be - side my - self with
tut - to a - mo - re è quel che
shows you tru - ly how she
fre - me e sma - nia dal fu -
jeal - ous ra - ges, fits of
fa, fre - mo e sma - nio
way. I am jeal - ous,
tut - to a - mo - re, tut - to a -
shows you tru - ly how she
tut - to a - mo - re, tut - to a -
shows me tru - ly how she
ro - re, u - na vec - chia me la
fu - ry! Be - ing tricked in such a
fa, tut - to a - mo - re è quel che
loves you; wo - men of - ten act that
ro - re, il de - sti - no glie la
fu - ry are the or - der of the
dal fu - ro - re, il de - sti - no me la
I am fur - ious, things have not turned out my
mo - re, tut - to a - mo - re è quel che
loves you, wo - men of - ten act that
mo - re, tut - to a - mo - re è quel che
loves me, wo - men of - ten act that

fa, fre - mo, sma - nio dal fu - ro - re, fre - mo, sma - nio dal fu -
way, tricked and cheat - ed by a spin - ster in a most dis - hon - est
fa, tut - to a - mo - re è quel che
way. Now you know how much she
fa, fre - me e sma - nia dal fu -
day, jeal - ous ra - ges, fits of
fa, fre - mo e sma - nio
way. I am jeal - ous,
fa, tut - to a - mo - re, tut - to a -
way. Now you know how much she
fa, tut - to a - mo - re, tut - to a -
way. Now I know how much she
ro - re, u - na vec - chia me la
fash - ion, in a most dis - taste - ful
fa, tut - to a - mo - re è quel che
loves you, wo - men of - ten act that
ro - re, il de - sti - no glie la
fu - ry are the or - der of the
dal fu - ro - re, il de - sti - no me la
I am fur - ious, things have not turned out my
mo - re, tut - to a - mo - re è quel che
loves you, wo - men of - ten act that
mo - re, tut - to a - mo - re è quel che
loves me, wo - men of - ten act that

fa, u - na vec - chia me la
way, in a most dis - taste - ful
fa, tut - to a - mo - re è quel che
way, wo - men of - ten, wo - men
fa, fre - me e sma - nia dal fu - ro - re, il de -
day, jeal - ous ra - ges, fits of fu - ry are the
fa, fre - mo e sma - nio dal fu - ro - re, il de -
way. I'm be - side my - self with fu - ry, things have
fa, tut - to a - mo - re è quel che
way, wo - men of - ten, wo - men
fa, tut - to a -
way, wo - men
mfp
mfp
fa, u - na vec - chia me la fa,
way, in a most dis - taste - ful way,
fa, è quel che fa, tut - to a -
of - ten act that way, wo - men
sti - no glie la fa, fre - me e sma - nia
or - der of the day, jeal - ous ra - ges,
sti - no me la fa, fre - mo e sma - nio dal fu -
not turned out my way. I'm be - side my - self with
fa, è quel che fa, tut - to a -
of - ten act that way, wo - men
mo - re e quel che fa,
of - ten act that way,
mfp

u - na vec - chia me la fa, u - na vec - chia me la fa.
in a most dis-taste-ful way, in a most dis-taste-ful way.
mo - re è quel che fa, è quel che fa.
of - ten, wo - men of - ten act that way.
dal fu - ro - re, il de - sti - no glie la fa.
fits of fu - ry are the or - der of the day.
ro - re, il de - sti - no me la fa.
fu - ry, things have not turned out my way.
mo - re è quel che fa, è quel che fa.
of - ten, wo - men of - ten act that way.
tut - to a - mo - re è quel che fa.
wo - men of - ten act that way.
mfp
Marcellina (Runs to embrace Susanna.)
Lo sde - gno cal - ma - te, mia ca - ra fi -
No long - er be an - gry, my dear lit - tle

gliuo - la. Sua ma - dre ab-brac - cia - te, che or vo - stra sa - rà, sua ma-dre ab-brac-
daugh - ter, from this mo-ment on - ward, I'm moth - er to you, for I___ am his
cia - te, che or vo - stra sa - rà.
moth-er and moth - er to you.
Susanna (to Bartolo)
Sua ma-dre?
His moth-er?
(to the Count)
sua ma-dre?
his moth-er?
Bartolo
Sua ma-dre!
His moth-er!
Count
Sua
His
ma - dre!
moth - er!
(to Don Curzio)
sua ma - dre?
his moth - er?
(to Marcellina)
sua ma - dre?
his moth - er?
Marcellina
Sua
His
Don Curzio
Sua ma - dre!
His moth - er!
tr

Susanna (to Figaro)
ma - dre, sua ma - dre! sua ma - dre! Tua ma - dre?
moth - er, his moth - er! his moth - er! Your moth - er?
Don Curzio
sua ma - dre! sua ma - dre!
His moth - er! his moth - er!
Count
sua ma - dre! sua ma - dre!
His moth - er! his moth - er!
Figaro
Bartolo
sua ma - dre! sua ma - dre! E
His moth - er! his moth - er! And
cresc.
p
quel - lo è mio pa - dre che a te lo di - rà, che a te lo di -
this is my fa - ther, he says so him-self, he says so him -

Susanna (to Bartolo)
(to the Count)
(to Don Curzio)
Suo pa-dre? suo pa-dre? suo pa-dre?
His fa-ther? his fa-ther? his fa-ther?
Don Curzio
Suo
His
Count
Suo pa-dre!
His fa-ther!
Bartolo
rà. Suo pa-dre!
self. His fa-ther!
tr
(to Marcellina)
suo pa - dre?
his fa - ther?
Marcellina
Suo pa - dre! suo pa - dre! suo
His fa - ther! his fa - ther! his
Don Curzio
pa - dre! suo pa - dre! suo
fa - ther! His fa - ther! his
Count
suo pa - dre! suo
His fa - ther! his
Bartolo
suo pa - dre! suo
His fa - ther! his
tr
cresc.
f

(to Figaro)
tuo pa - dre?
Your fa - ther?
pa - dre!
fa - ther!
pa - dre!
fa - ther!
pa - dre!
fa - ther!
Figaro
pa - dre!
fa - ther!
E quel-la è mia ma - dre che a te lo di - rà, che a
And this is my moth - er, she'll tell you I'm right, just
p
(All four rush to embrace each other.)
te lo di - rà, mia ma - dre che a te lo di - rà, mio pa - dre che a
ask her your - self, my moth - er, just ask her your - self, my fa - ther, he'll

Susanna sotto voce
Al
In
Marcellina sotto voce
Al dol - ce, al
In one — bless - ed
Don Curzio sotto voce
Al fie - ro tor-men - to di que - sto mo-men - to,
In one curs - ed mo - ment his plans have been thwart - ed,
Count sotto voce
Al fie - ro tor-men - to di que - sto mo-men - to, al
In one curs - ed mo - ment my plans have been thwart - ed, it
Bartolo sotto voce
Al dol - ce, al
In one — bless - ed
Figaro
sotto
te lo di - rà.
tell you I'm right.
Al
In
pp
dol - ce con - ten - to di ques - to mo -
one — bless - ed mo - ment our fears — have been
dol - ce con - ten - to di ques - to mo -
mo - ment our fears — have been thwart - ed, a
al fie - ro tor-men - to di ques - to
it fills him with en - vy and bit - ter
fie - ro tor - men - to di ques - to mo -
fills me with en - vy and bit - ter re -
dol - ce con - ten - to di ques - to mo -
mo - ment our fears — have been thwart - ed, a
voce
dol - ce con - ten - to di ques - to mo -
one bless - ed mo - ment our fears have been

men - to, quest' a - ni - ma ap - pe - na re -
thwart - ed, a hap - pi - er fu - ture at
men - to, quest' a - ni - ma ap - pe - na re -
hap - pi - er, a hap - pi - er fu - ture at
mo - men - to, quest' a - ni - ma ap - pe - na
re - sent - ment, to see them all so hap - py
men - to, quest' a - ni - ma ap - pe - na re -
sent - ment, to see them all so hap - py with
men - to, quest' a - ni - ma ap - pe - na re -
hap - pi - er, a hap - pi - er fu - ture at
men - to, quest' a - ni - ma ap - pe - na re -
thwart - ed, a hap - pi - er fu - ture at
si - ster or sà, al dol - ce con -
last is in sight. In one bless - ed
si - ster or sà, al dol - ce con -
last is in sight. In one bless - ed
re - si - ster or sà, al fie - ro tor - men - to
with sud - den de - light. In one curs - ed mo - ment
si - ster or sà, al fie - ro tor - men - to
sud - den de - light. In one curs - ed mo - ment
si - ster or sà, al dol - ce con -
last is in sight. In one bless - ed
si - ster or sà, al dol - ce con -
last is in sight. In one bless - ed

ten - to di que - sto mo - men - to,
mo - ment our fears have been thwart - ed,
ten - to di que - sto mo - men - to,
mo - ment our fears have been thwart - ed,
di que - sto mo - men - to, quest a - ni - ma ap -
his plans have been thwart - ed, not e - ven the
di que - sto mo - men - to, quest' a - ni - ma ap -
my plans have been thwart - ed, not e - ven the
ten - to di que - sto mo - men - to,
mo - ment our fears have been thwart - ed,
ten - to di que - sto mo - men - to,
mo - ment our fears have been thwart - ed,
f
p
f
quest' a - ni - ma ap - pe - na re -
a hap - pi - er fu - ture at
quest' a - ni - ma ap - pe - na re -
a hap - pi - er fu - ture at
pe - na re - si - ster or sà,
hope of re - venge is in sight,
pe - na re - si - ster or sà,
hope of re - venge is in sight,
quest' a - ni - ma ap - pe - na re -
a hap - pi - er fu - ture at
quest' a - ni - ma ap - pe - na re -
a hap - pi - er fu - ture at
p

si - ster or sà, quest' a - ni - ma ap -
last is in sight, a hap - pi - er
si - ster or sà, quest' a - ni - ma ap -
last is in sight, a hap - pi - er
quest' a - ni - ma ap - pe - na re - si - ster or sà,
not e - ven the hope of re-venge is in sight.
quest' a - ni - ma ap - pe - na re - si - ster or sà,
not e - ven the hope of re-venge is in sight.
si - ster or sa, quest' a - ni - ma ap -
last is in sight, a hap - pi - er
si - ster or sa, quest' a - ni - ma ap -
last is in sight, a hap - pi - er
f
f
f
p
pe - na re - si - ster or sà, ap -
fu - ture at last is in sight, at
pe - na re - si - ster or sà, ap -
fu - ture at last is in sight, at
sotto voce
al fie - ro tor - men - to di que - sto mo -
In one curs - ed mo - ment his plans have been
sotto voce
al fie - ro tor - men - to di que - sto mo -
In one curs - ed mo - ment my plans have been
pe - na re - si - ster or sà,
fu - ture at last is in sight,
pe - na re - si - ster or sà,
fu - ture at last is in sight,

pe - na re - si - ster or
last is in sight, yes, a
pe - na re - si - ster or
last is in sight, yes, a
men - to, quest' a - ni - ma ap - pe - na re - si - ster or
thwart - ed, not e - ven the hope of re - venge is in
men - to, quest' a - ni - ma ap - pe - na re - si - ster or
thwart - ed, not e - ven the hope of re - venge is in
re - si - ster or
at last is in
re - si - ster or
at last is in
sà, ap - pe - na re - si - ster or
hap - py fu - ture at last is in
sà, ap - pe - na re - si - ster or
hap - py fu - ture at last is in
sà, al fie - ro tor - men - to quest' a - ni - ma ap - pe - na re - si - ster or
sight, it fills him with en - vy to see them so hap - py with sud - den de -
sà, al fie - ro tor - men - to quest' a - ni - ma ap - pe - na re - si - ster or
sight, it fills me with en - vy to see them so hap - py with sud - den de -
sà, re - si - ster or
sight, at last is in
sà, re - si - ster or
sight, at last is in

sà, quest' a - ni - ma ap - pe - na re - si - ster or
sight, a hap - pi - er fu - ture at last is in
light, to see them so hap - py with sud - den de -
sà, re - si - ster or
sight, at last is in
sà, quest' a - ni - ma ap - pe - na re - si - ster or
light, to see them so hap - py with sud - den de -

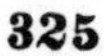

sà, re - si - ster or sà.
sight, at last is in sight.
sà, re - si - ster or sà.
sight, at last is in sight.
(Exeunt the Count and Don Curzio.)
sà, quest' a - ni-ma ap - pe - na re - si - ster or sà.
light, to see them so hap - py with sud - den de - light.
sà, quest' a - ni-ma ap - pe - na re - si - ster or sà.
light, to see them so hap - py with sud - den de - light.
sà, re - si - ster or sà.
sight, at last is in sight.
sà, re - si - ster or sà.
sight, at last is in sight.
f
tr

Recitative

Marcellina, Bartolo, Susanna, and Figaro

Susanna
(Throws a
gliet - to del de - nar che a me de - vi, ed è tua do - te. Pren - di an -
note for the mon - ey you owe me. Take it as dow - ry. Take this
purse to the ground.)
Bartolo (Does the same.)
Figaro
cor que - sta bor - sa. E que - sta an - co - ra. Bra - vi! git - ta - te pur, c'hio pi - glio o -
purse in ad - di - tion. And al - so this one. Thank you! Just keep right on, I'm get - ting
Susanna
gno - ra. Vo - lia - mo ad in - for - mar d'o - gni av - ven - tu - ra Ma - da - ma, e no - stro
wealth - y. Now let us go and tell all that has happened to the Count - ess and un - cle An -
Figaro
Bartolo
zi - o. Chi al par di me con - ten - ta. Chi al par di me con - ten - ta! I - o! I - o!
to - nio. Who is as glad as I am? Who is as glad as I am! I am! I am!
Marcellina
Susanna
Marcellina
pp
cresc.
f
pp
I - o! E schiat - ti il si - gnor Con - te al gu - sto mi - o!
I am! The Count is wild with fu - ry, but we don't care a bit!
Bartolo
Figaro
pp
cresc.
f
pp
E schiat - ti il si - gnor Con - te al gu - sto mi - o!
The Count is wild with fu - ry, but we don't care a bit!
Andante
a tempo
p
cresc.
f
p
(All exeunt, embracing.)

Recitative

Barbarina and Cherubino

(Enter Barbarina and Cherubino.)

Barbarina
sai che par-ti-to ei mi cre-de per Si - vi-glia. O ve' che ma-ra-
know, he be-lieves I have left for Se - ville. Since when does that dis-
vi - glia! e se ti tro - va, non sa - rà co - sa
turb you? And if he found you, it would not be the
nuo - va. O - di... vo - glia - mo ve-stir-ti co-me no - i, tut-te in-
first time. Lis - ten: You must let us dress you like a girl. Then we
siem an-drem poi a pre-sen-tar de' fio-ri a Ma - da - mi - na;
all will pre - sent a nice bou-quet of flow-ers to the Coun-tess.
(Exeunt.)
fi - da-ti,o Che - ru - bin, di Bar - ba - ri - na.
Just leave it all to me, your Bar - ba - ri - na.

No. 19. E Susanna non vien!... Dove sono i bei momenti

And Susanna is late... Are they over, those cherished moments

Recitative and Aria

Countess

va-ce e ge-lo-so!
pul-sive and so jeal-ous!
Ma che mal c'è?
But what's the harm?
can-gian-do i miei ve-
I on-ly want to
Allegretto
[Andante]
sti - ti con quel-li di Su - san-na, e i suoi co' mie - i al fa-vor del-la
meet him in a dress of Su-san-na's while she wears mine, by the fa-vor of
not - te.
dark - ness.
oh cie-lo! a qual u-mil sta - to fa-ta - le
Ah, Heav-en! To what shameful state of ex-is-tence
io son ri-dot-ta da un con-sor-te cru-del!
have I de-scend-ed through the fault of my hus-band,
Che do-po a-
who, af - ter

ver-mi con un mi-sto in-au-di - to d'in - fe - del - tà, di ge - lo - si - a, di
treat-ing me with scorn un-ex-am-pled and with dis - dain, with jeal-ous ra-ges be -
sde - gno! Pri - ma a - ma - ta, in - di of - fe - sa, e al - fin tra -
trayed me, first be - lov - ed, then of - fend - ed, at last de -
di - ta, fam - mi or cer - car da u - na mia ser - va a - i - ta!
sert - ed, forced me to plead now for my maid's as - sis - tance!
Andantino
Do - ve so - no i bei mo - men - ti, di dol -
Are they o - ver, those cher - ished mo - ments, hours to -

cez-za e di_ pia - cer,_ do - ve an - da - ro
geth-er so sweet-ly_ shared? Are they bro - ken,
dolce
i giu - ra - men - ti di quel lab - bro_ men - zo -
those fer - vent pled - ges, his de - ceit - ful_ lips de -
gner, di quel lab - bro men - zo - gner!
clared, his de - ceit - ful_ lips de - clared?
Per-chè mai, se in pian-ti e in pe - ne per me
If a bit - ter_ fate in - clined me such un -

tut - to si can - giò, per me tut - to si can - giò, la me-
hap - pi-ness to know, such un - hap - pi - ness to know, why do
fp
mo - ria di quel be - ne dal mio sen non tra - pas - sò,
mem - o - ries re - mind me of those joys of long a - go,
la me - mo - ria di quel ben non tra - pas - sò?
why do mem - o - ries re - call those joys of long a - go?
Do - ve so - no i bei mo - men - ti di dol-
Are they o - ver, those cher - ished mo - ments, hours to-

cez-za e di pia - cer,
geth-er so sweet-ly shared?
do - vean - da - ro i
Are they bro - ken, those
dolce
giu - ra - men - ti di quel lab - bro men - zo - gner!
fer - vent pled - ges his de - ceit - ful lips de - clared?
sf
Allegro
Ah! se al-men la mia co - stan-za nel lan - gui - re a - man - doo -
If at last my heart's de - vo - tion could a - chieve but one re -
p
gnor, mi por - tas - se u - na spe - ran - za di can - giar l'in - gra - to
ward, and re - vive the dead e - mo - tion of my false and heart - less

cor, di can - giar l'in - gra - to cor.
lord, of my false and heart - less lord.
f
sf
p
Ah! se al - men la _ mia co - stan - za,
Ah! if at last my heart's de - vo - tion,
f
sf
f
sf
p
Ah! se al - men la _ mia co -
Ah! if at last my heart's de -
stan - za, nel lan - gui - re a - man - do o - gnor, _ mi por -
vo - tion could a - chieve but _ one re - ward, _ and re -

tas - se u - na spe - ran - za di can - giar l'in - gra - to cor, mi por -
vive the dead e - mo - tion of my false and heart-less lord, and a -
tas - se u - na spe - ran - za di can - giar
wak - en the dead e - mo - tion of my false
l'in - gra - to cor, di can - giar
and heart - less lord, of my false
l'in - gra - to cor, di can - giar l'in -
and heart - less lord, of my false and
p

gra - to cor, di can- giar l'in- gra - -
heart - less lord, of my false and heart - -
tr
- - to cor, l'in - gra - to_ cor, l'in -
- - less lord, my heart - less lord, my
fp
fp
fp
fp
cresc.
(Exit.)
gra - to cor.
heart - less lord.
f
3
3

Recitative

Antonio, Count, Countess, and Susanna

(Enter the Count, and Antonio, with a hat in his hand.)

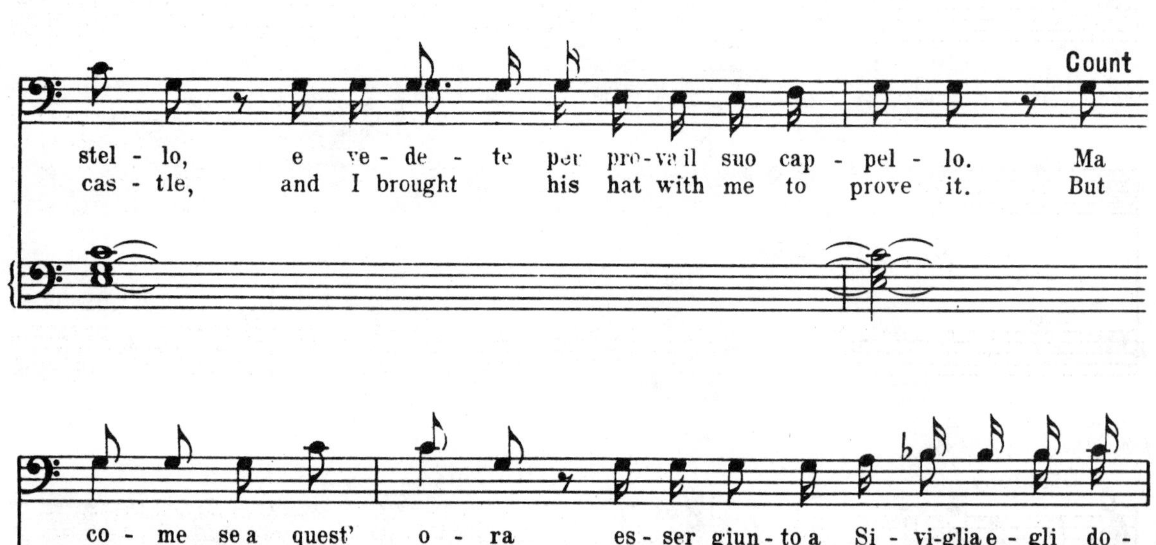

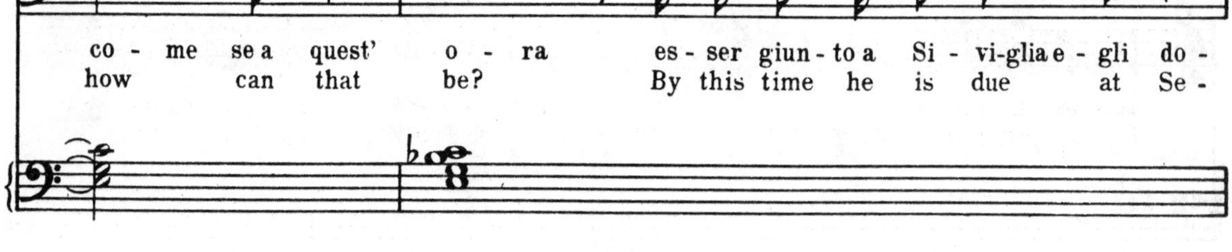

Là ve - stis - si da don - na, e là la -
There they dressed him in girls' clothes, and there he
Count
Antonio
scia - ti ha gl'al-tri a - bi - ti suoi. Per - fi - di! An - diam,
al - so has left his new u - ni - form. Rep - ro - bates! Please come,
(Exeunt.)
(Enter the Countess and Susanna.)
e li ve - dre - te vo - i.
and I'll be glad to show you.
Countess
Susanna
Co - sa mi nar - ri? e che ne dis - se il Con - te? Gli si leg - ge - va in
Is - n't that mar-vel-ous? What was the Count's re - ac - tion? Oh, he was so
Countess
fron - te il di - spet - to, e la rab - bia. Pia - no, che me - glio
fu - rious that he hard - ly could bear it. Was he! So much the

or lo por-re-mo in gab-bia! Dov' è l'ap-pun-ta-men-to che
bet-ter for our in-ten-tions. And where is the ap-point-ment which
Susanna
Countess
tu gli pro-po-ne-sti? In giar-di-no. Fis-siam-gli un
you pro-posed to give him? In the gar-den. Be more spe-
Susanna
lo-co. Scri-vi. Ch'io scri-va, ma si-
cif-ic. Write to him. But is that not too
Countess
(Susanna sits down and writes.)
gno-ra... Eh scri-vi, di-co, e tut-to io pren-do su me
dar-ing? Do as I tell you, let all the blame fall on my
(dictating)
stes-sa: Can-zo-net-ta sull' a-ria.
shoul-ders. Write a mes-sage "to Ro-meo."

No. 20. Sull' aria

"To Romeo"

Duettino

Susanna and Countess

(enquiringly)
sot-to i pi - ni?
pines are grow-ing?
pi - ni del bo-schet-to—
grove where pines are grow-ing,
sot-to i
In the
(writing)
Sot-to i pi - ni del bo-
In the grove where. . . pines are
pi - ni del bo-schet-to,
grove where pines are grow - ing,"
schet-to,
grow-ing."
Cer-to, cer-to il ca - pi - rà,
Yes, the rest he will re - call.
Ei già il re - sto ca - pi - rà.
And the rest he will re - call.

(They read the letter together.)
cer - to, cer - to il ca - pi - rà.
And the rest he will re - call.
Ei già il re - sto ca - pi - rà.
And the rest he will re - call.
Can-zo-net-ta sull'
Let us read it to-
Che so - a - ve ze - fi - ret - to,
"When the breeze is gent - ly blow - ing,
a - ria.
geth - er.
que - sta se - ra spi - re-
"and the eve - ning shad - ows
Sot - to i pi - ni del bo - schet - to.
In the grove where pines are grow - ing."
Cer - to, cer - to il ca - pi-
and the rest he will re-
rà.
fall,"
Ei già il re - sto ca - pi - rà,
and the rest he will re - call,
il
he

rà, il ca - pi - rà, cer - to, cer - to il
call, he will re - call, yes, the rest he
ca - pi - rà, ei già il re - sto
will re - call, yes, the rest he
ca - pi - rà, cer - to, cer - to il ca - pi - rà, il ca - pi -
will re - call, yes, the rest he will re - call, he will re -
ca - pi - rà, ei già il re - sto ca - pi - rà,
will re - call, yes, the rest he will re - call,
rà, il ca - pi - rà, il ca - pi - rà, il ca - pi -
call, he will re - call, he will re - call, he will re -
il ca - pi - rà, il ca - pi - rà, il ca - pi - rà, il ca - pi -
he will re - call, he will re - call, he will re - call, he will re -

(Folds the letter.)
rà. Pie-gato è il fo - glio, or co - me si si - gil - la?
call. The note is read - y, and how shall we seal it?
(Draws a
rà. Ec - co,
call. This way!
pin and gives it to her.)
Countess
pren - di u - na spil - la, ser - vi - rà di si - gil - lo. At -
Let's take a pin, we will use that to seal it. And
ten - di, scri - vi sul ri - ver - so del fo - glio; "Ri - man -
fur - ther write on the back of the let - ter; "Re -
Susanna
da - te il si - gil - lo." È più bi - zar - ro di quel del - la pa -
turn the pin, please." That's an i - de - a! It makes it sound mys -
Countess
(Susanna puts the note in her bosom.)
ten - te. Pre - sto na - scon - di; io sen - to ve - nir gen - te.
ter - ious. Hur - ry and hide it! I hear some-bod - y com - ing.

No. 21. Ricevete, o padroncina

Mistress dear, accept these flowers

Chorus

Country girls

(Enter Cherubino, dressed as a country girl; and Barbarina, with several other country girls, dressed in the same way, carrying nosegays.)

tan - te con - ta - di - ne, e siam tut - te po - ve - ri - ne, ma quel
poor and sim - ple peas - ants, please ac - cept these hum-ble pres - ents as a
po - co che re - chia - mo ve lo dia - mo di buon cor, ve lo
to - ken of af - fec - tion from our hearts so loyal and true, from our
dia - mo di buon cor, di buon cor, di buon cor, ve lo dia - mo di buon
hearts so loyal and true, from our hearts, from our hearts from our hearts so loy-al and
cor.
true.

Recitative

Barbarina, Countess, Susanna, Antonio, Count, and Cherubino

Barbarina
l'a - ria si mo - de - sta?
looks so shy and mod - est!
Ell' è u - na mia cu - gi - na e per le
That one? She is my cous - in, she came last
noz - ze è ve - nu - ta jer se - ra.
night to be here for the wed - ding.
Countess
O - no - ria - mo la bel - la fo - re -
Let us hon - or our guest on her ar -
(Takes Cherubino's flowers and
stie - ra, ve - ni - te quì,
ri - val. Come here to me,
da - te - mi i vo - stri
may I ac - cept your
kisses him on the forehead.)
fio - ri. Come ar-ros - sì!
flow - ers? Look at her blush!
Su - san - na, e non ti pa - re. . . che so -
Su - san - na, do you not no - tice a re -
mi - gli ad al - cu - no?
sem - blance to some one?
Susanna
Al na - tu - ra - le.
Yes, it is strik - ing.

(Antonio enters stealthily, pulls off Cherubino's bonnet, and puts his officer's cap on him.)
Antonio
Countess
Susanna
Eh co-spet-tac-cio! è que-sti l'uf-fi - zia - le! Oh stel - le! (Ma-lan-
What do you know! If that's not Che-ru - bi - no! Good Heav-ens! What a
Count
Countess
dri - no!) Eb-ben, Ma-da - ma! Io so-no, o si - gnor mi - o, ir - ri -
dev - il! What now, my la - dy! This time, my dear hus-band, I'm an-
Count
Countess
ta-ta e sor-pre-sa al par di vo - i. Ma sta-ma-ne? Sta -
noyed and as-ton-ished as much as you are. But this morn-ing? This
ma - ne per l'o-dier-na fe - sta vo-le-vam tra-ve-stir-lo al mo - do
morn-ing we were get-ting read-y for to-night's cel-e-bra-tion and we
Count
stes - so, che l'han ve-sti-to a - des - so. E per-chè non par -
dressed him ex-act - ly as you see him. And why have you not

Cherubino (tearing his cap off his head)
Count
ti - sti? Si - gnor... Sa - prò pu - ni - re la tua dis - ub - bi -
left? My lord... I'll have you pun - ished for in - sub - or - di -
Barbarina
dien - za. Ec - cel - len - za! Ec - cel - len - za! voi mi di - te sì
na - tion! Dear-est mas - ter, dear-est mas - ter, ev - 'ry time when you
spes - so qual vol - ta m'ab-brac-cia - te, e mi ba - cia - te: "Bar-ba-ri - na, se
kissed me, do you re-mem-ber, you al-ways told me: "Bar-ba-ri - na, if you
Count
Barbarina
m'a - mi, ti da - rò quel che bra - mi." Io dis - si que - sto? Vo - i,
love me, there's no wish I won't grant you!" So, did I say that? Sure - ly!
or da - te - mi, pa - dro - ne, in spo - so Che - ru - bi - no, e v'a - me - rò, com'
Now, dear-est mas-ter, let me mar-ry Che - ru - bi - no, and in re - turn I'll

Countess (to the Count)
Antonio
a-mo il mio gat-ti-no. Eb-be-ne, or toc-ca a vo-i. Bra-va, fi-
love you like my kit-ten. My lord, it's up to you now. Well said, my
Count (aside)
gliuo-la! hai buon ma-e-stro, che ti fa la sco-la. (Non sò, qual uom, qual
daugh-ter! One can see you had an ex-pert teach-er. (I'd like to know what
de-mo-ne, qual Di-o, ri-vol-ga tut-to quan-to a tor-to mi-o.)
nem-e-sis, what de-mon con-verts each sit-u-a-tion to my un-do-ing?)
Figaro (Enters.)
Si-gnor, se trat-te-ne-te tut-te que-ste ra-gaz-ze, ad-dio
My lord, if you de-tain these girls here ver-y much long-er, good-bye
Count
fe-ste, ad-dio dan-za. E che? vor-re-sti bal-lar col piè stra-
par-ty, good-bye danc-ing! What's that? You're plan-ning to dance with your twist-ed

Figaro (Pretends to straighten his leg, then tries to dance.) (Calls all the girls, starts
vol - to? Eh non mi duol più mol - to. An - diam, bel - le fan -
foot? It does not hurt at all now; come on, girls, let's be
to go; the Count calls him back.)
Countess (to Susanna)
Susanna (to the Countess)
ciul - le. (Co - me si ca - ve - rà dall' im - ba - raz - zo?) La - scia - te fa - re a
go - ing. (Now how will he get out of this pre - dic - a - ment?) Oh, don't be con-cerned a -
Count
Figaro
lu - i. Per buo - na sor - te i va - si e - ran di cre - ta. Sen - za
bout him! It's ver - y luck - y the flow - er - bed was a soft one. Ver - y
(as above)
Antonio (Holds him back.)
fal - lo. An - dia - mo dun - que, an - dia - mo. E in - tan - to a ca - val - lo
luck - y. No more de - lay - ing, let's go now. And mean-while, on horse-back,
Figaro
di ga - lop - po a Si - vi - glia an - da - va il pag - gio. Di ga - lop - po, o di
Che - ru - bi - no was gal - lop - ing to Se - ville. May - be gal - lop - ing, may - be

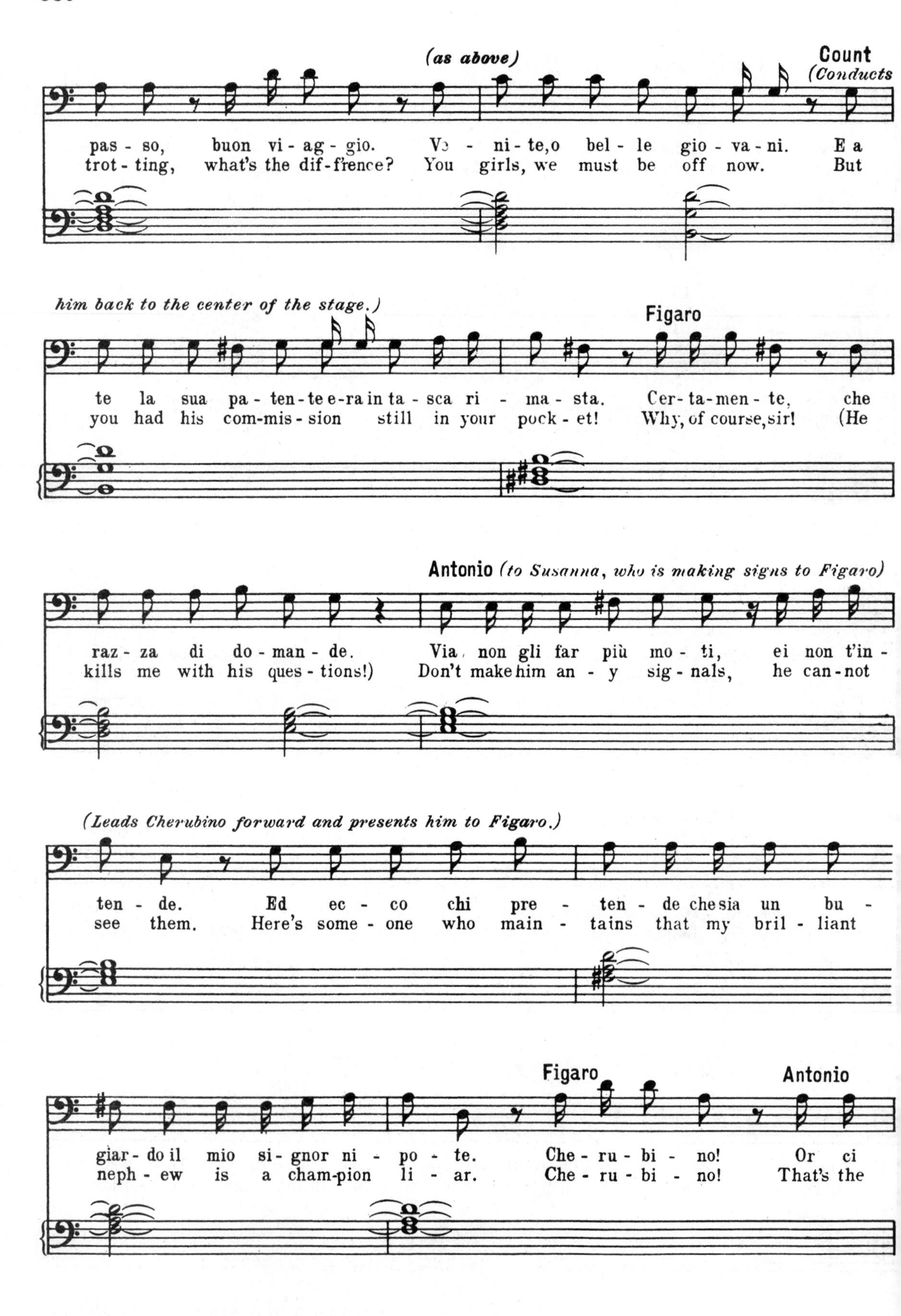
(as above)
Count
(Conducts
pas - so, buon vi - ag - gio. Ve - ni - te,o bel - le gio - va - ni. E a
trot - ting, what's the dif - f'rence? You girls, we must be off now. But
him back to the center of the stage.)
Figaro
te la sua pa - ten - te e - ra in ta - sca ri - ma - sta. Cer - ta - men - te, che
you had his com - mis - sion still in your pock - et! Why, of course, sir! (He
Antonio (to Susanna, who is making signs to Figaro)
raz - za di do - man - de. Via, non gli far più mo - ti, ei non t'in -
kills me with his ques - tions!) Don't make him an - y sig - nals, he can - not
(Leads Cherubino forward and presents him to Figaro.)
ten - de. Ed ec - co chi pre - ten - de che sia un bu -
see them. Here's some - one who main - tains that my bril - liant
Figaro
Antonio
giar - do il mio si - gnor ni - po - te. Che - ru - bi - no! Or ci
neph - ew is a cham - pion li - ar. Che - ru - bi - no! That's the

(The Spanish march is heard in the distance.)

Finale of Act III

No. 22. Ecco la marcia
There's the procession
Figaro, Susanna, Countess, Count, and Chorus

is heard more and more clearly.)
Countess
tes-sa! Or non par-lia-mo. Ec-co qui le due noz-ze, ri-ce-ver-le dob-
la-dy! Let's not dis-cuss it. Both the coup-les are com-ing, we must re-ceive them
biam, al-fin si trat-ta d'una vo-stra pro-tet-ta. Seg-
well, at least in one bride you have shown spe-cial in-t'rest. Be
Count
gia-mo! Seg-gia-mo! (e me-di-tiam ven-
seat-ed! With plea-sure! (and plan a fit-ting
(The Count and Countess seat themselves on the thrones. Enter Figaro, Susanna,
det-ta.)
ven-geance.)
tr
tr
un poco cresc.

Marcellina, Barbarina, Bartolo, Antonio, hunters with guns, court attendants, and country people. Two girls bring the little bridal hat with white plumes, two others a white veil, and two others still gloves and a nosegay. They are followed by Figaro with Marcellina. Two other girls carry a similar hat for Susanna, etc., followed by Bartolo with Susanna. Bartolo leads Susanna to the Count, and she kneels to receive from him the hat, etc. Figaro leads Marcellina to the Countess for the same purpose.)

Allegretto
p
tr

tr
Two Young Girls
A - man - ti co - stan - ti se - gua - ci d'o -
Oh, come, faith - ful lov - ers, in hap - py ac -
nor, can - ta - te, lo - da - te sì sag - gio si -
cord, and grate - ful - ly join __ us in praise of our
gnor, A - man - ti co - stan - ti se - gua - ci d'o -
lord. The right of his for - bears he kind - ly ig -

nor, can - ta - te, lo - da - te sì sag - gio si -
nored, re - vok - ing a cus - tom his sub - jects ab -
tr
tr
tr
gnor, can - ta - te, lo - da - te sì sag - gio si -
horred. Oh, come, lift your voic - es in praise of our
tr
tr
tr
gnor. A un drit - to ce - den - do,
lord. A prac - tice he end - ed
tr
tr
tr
che ol - trag - gia, che of - fen - de,
which shamed and of - fend - ed,
tr
tr
tr
tr

ei ca - ste vi ren - de ai vo - stri a - ma -
and leaves chaste and spot - less the one you a -
tor, a un drit - to ce - den - do, che ol - trag - gia, che of -
dored, a prac - tice he end - ed which shamed and of -
fen - de, ei ca - ste vi ren - de ai vo - stri a - ma -
fend - ed, and leaves chaste and spot - less the one you a -
tor, ei ca - ste vi ren - de ai vo - stri a - ma -
dored. Come all, lift your voic - es in praise of our

tor.
lord.
Soprano
Alto
Can - tia - mo, lo - dia - mo sì sag - gio si -
With hearts ev - er grate - ful we sing to our
Tenor
Can - tia - mo, lo - dia - mo sì sag - gio si -
With hearts ev - er grate - ful we sing to our
Bass
Can - tia - mo, lo - dia - mo sì sag - gio si -
With hearts ev - er grate - ful we sing to our
f
gnor, can - tia - mo, lo - dia - mo sì sag - gio si -
lord, and may Heav - en's bless - ing his wis - dom re -
gnor, can - tia - mo, lo - dia - mo sì sag - gio si -
lord, and may Heav - en's bless - ing his wis - dom re -
gnor, can - tia - mo, lo - dia - mo sì sag - gio si -
lord, and may Heav - en's bless - ing his wis - dom re -

gnor, sì sag - gio si - gnor, sì sag - gio si -
ward, his wis - dom re - ward, his wis - dom re -
gnor, sì sag - gio si - gnor, sì sag - gio si -
ward, his wis - dom re - ward, his wis - dom re -
gnor, sì sag - gio si - gnor, sì sag - gio si -
ward, his wis - dom re - ward, his wis - dom re -
(A dance is begun.)
Andante
gnor, sì sag - gio si - gnor.
ward, his wis - dom re - ward.
gnor, sì sag - gio si - gnor.
ward, his wis - dom re - ward.
gnor, sì sag - gio si - gnor.
ward, his wis - dom re - ward.
Andante
tr
p

(Susanna, kneeling during the duet, plucks the Count's sleeve, shows him the note, then reaches to her head in a manner visible to the audience, and while the Count pretends to adjust her bonnet, she

gives him the note. The Count quickly hides it, and Susanna rises and curtseys. Figaro comes to receive her, and they dance the Fandango. Marcellina rises a little later. Bartolo receives her

from the Countess.)

(Takes out the note and pricks his finger with the pin as he
Count
Eh, già so-li-ta u-san-za, le don-ne fic-can
I won-der why these care-less fe-males must fas-ten all they
tr
tr
opens it. He shakes his finger, squeezes it, sucks it, and throws the pin to the ground.)
gli a-ghi in o-gni lo-co, ah! ah! ca-pi-sco il
han-dle with pins and need-les! Ha, ha! I get the
tr
tr
Figaro (Sees it all and says to Susanna)
gio-co! Un bi-gliet-to a-mo-ro-so che gli diè nel pas-sar qual-che ga-
point now! Just a note of af-fec-tion which some la-dy has giv-en him in
lan-te, ed e-ra si-gil-la-to d'u-na
pass-ing. She must have used a pin to seal the

(The Count reads the note,
spil - la, ond' ei si pun - se il di - to,
let - ter, see, and now he stuck his fin - ger;
tr
kisses it, looks for the pin, finds it, and sticks it in his lapel.)
il Nar - cis - so or la cer - ca, oh che stor - di - to!
now he's try - ing to find it. Oh, is he stu - pid!
tr
Recit.
Count
An - da - te, a - mi - ci! e sia per que - sta se - ra di -
Dear friends and sub - jects, I'll see you all this eve - ning, to -
Maestoso

spos - to l'ap-pa-ra - to nu-zia - le col - la più ric - ca pom - pa! io vo' che
night we'll cel - e-brate the doub-le wed-ding with the great - est of splen - dor. For this must
si - a ma-gni-fi - ca la fe - sta, e can - ti, e fuo - chi, e gran
be a mag-nif - i-cent oc - ca - sion, with mu - sic and fire-works and a
ce - na, e gran bal - lo: e o - gnu-no im - pa - ri, com' io
ban - quet, al - so danc - ing: so I may show you how much
trat - to co - lor che a me son ca - ri.
love and good - will I feel I owe you.

Allegretto
Soprano sotto voce
Alto sotto voce
A - man - ti co - stan - ti se - gua - ci d'o -
Oh, come, faith - ful lov - ers, in hap - py ac -
Tenor sotto voce
A - man - ti co - stan - ti se - gua - ci d'o -
Oh, come, faith - ful lov - ers, in hap - py ac -
Bass sotto voce
A - man - ti co - stan - ti se - gua - ci d'o -
Oh, come, faith - ful lov - ers, in hap - py ac -
Allegretto
p
tr
nor, can - ta - te, lo - da - te sì sag - gio si -
cord, and grate - ful - ly join us in praise of our
nor, can - ta - te, lo - da - te sì sag - gio si -
cord, and grate - ful - ly join us in praise of our
nor, can - ta - te, lo - da - te sì sag - gio si -
cord, and grate - ful - ly join us in praise of our
tr

gnor. A un drit - to ce - den - do, ch'ol - trag - gia, ch'of -
lord. A prac - tice he end - ed, which shamed and of -
gnor. A un drit - to ce - den - do, ch'ol - trag - gia, ch'of -
lord. A prac - tice he end - ed, which shamed and of -
gnor. A un drit - to ce - den - do, ch'ol - trag - gia, ch'of -
lord. A prac - tice he end - ed, which shamed and of -
fen - de, ei ca - ste vi ren - de ai vo - stri a - ma -
fend - ed, and leaves chaste and spot - less the one you a -
fen - de, ei ca - ste vi ren - de ai vo - stri a - ma -
fend - ed, and leaves chaste and spot - less the one you a -
fen - de, ei ca - ste vi ren - de ai vo - stri a - ma -
fend - ed, and leaves chaste and spot - less the one you a -
tr
tr

tor, ei ca - ste vi ren - de ai vo - stri a - ma - tor. Can-
dored. Come, all, lift your voic - es in praise of our lord. With
tor, ei ca - ste vi ren - de ai vo - stri a - ma - tor. Can-
dored. Come, all, lift your voic - es in praise of our lord. With
tor, ei ca - ste vi ren - de ai vo - stri a - ma - tor. Can-
dored. Come, all, lift your voic - es in praise of our lord. With
tia - mo, lo - dia - mo sì sag - gio si - gnor, can - tia - mo, lo-
hearts ev - er grate - ful we sing to our lord, and may Heav - en's
tia - mo, lo - dia - mo sì sag - gio si - gnor, can - tia - mo, lo-
hearts ev - er grate - ful we sing to our lord, and may Heav - en's
tia - mo, lo - dia - mo sì sag - gio si - gnor, can - tia - mo, lo-
hearts ev - er grate - ful we sing to our lord, and may Heav - en's

End of Act III

Act IV

(Scene: *A small room*)

No. 23. L'ho perduta, me meschina!

I have lost it, Heaven help me!

Cavatina

Barbarina

du - ta! me-schi - nel - la! ah chi sa_do-ve_sa - rà?
aw - ful, sim-ply aw - ful! Oh, what troub-le I_am in!
Non la tro - vo, ah non la tro - vo! me-schi -
I keep look-ing, but can - not find it, this is
nel - la! l'ho per-du - ta! ah chi sa_do-ve_sa - rà! E mia cu-
dread - ful! I am des - p'rate, this is my_un-luck - y day! Cous-in Su-
a piacere
gi - na, e il pa-dron, co - sa di - rà? co - sa di - rà?
san - na, and the Count— what will they say? What will they say?

Recitative

Figaro, Barbarina, and Marcellina

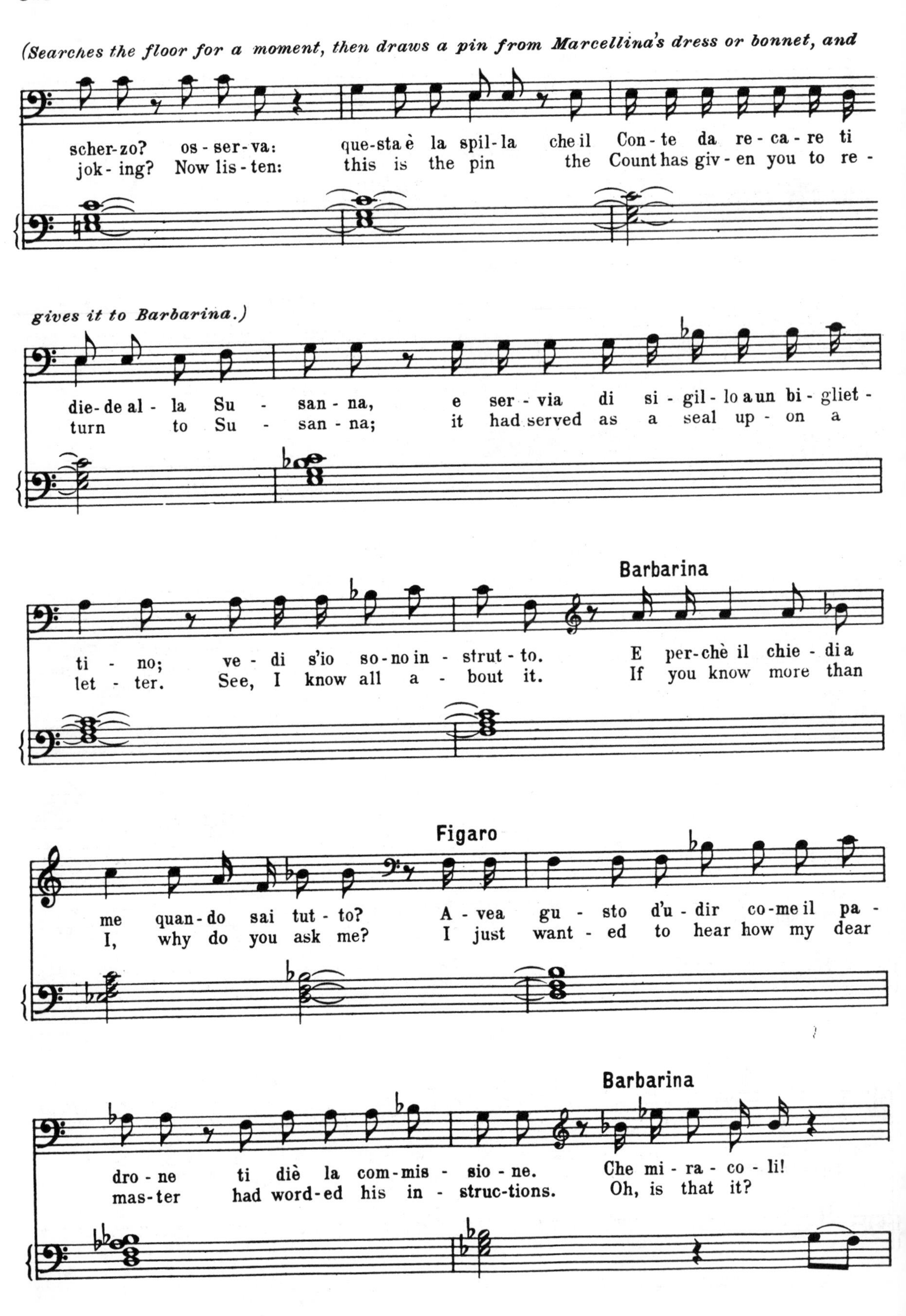
(Searches the floor for a moment, then draws a pin from Marcellina's dress or bonnet, and
scher-zo? os-ser-va: que-sta è la spil-la che il Con-te da re-ca-re ti
jok-ing? Now lis-ten: this is the pin the Count has giv-en you to re-
gives it to Barbarina.)
die-de al-la Su-san-na, e ser-via di si-gil-lo a un bi-gliet-
turn to Su-san-na; it had served as a seal up-on a
ti-no; ve-di s'io so-no in-strut-to.
let-ter. See, I know all a-bout it.
Barbarina
E per-chè il chie-di a
If you know more than
me quan-do sai tut-to?
I, why do you ask me?
Figaro
A-vea gu-sto d'u-dir co-me il pa-
I just want-ed to hear how my dear
dro-ne ti diè la com-mis-sio-ne.
mas-ter had word-ed his in-struc-tions.
Barbarina
Che mi-ra-co-li!
Oh, is that it?

"Tie - ni, fan-ciul - la, re - ca que - sta spil - la a la bel - la Su - san - na,
"Please, Bar - ba - ri - na, take this lit - tle pin here, bring it back to Su - san - na,
Figaro
Barbarina
e dil - le: que - sto è il si - gil - lo de' pi - ni!" Ah! ah! de' pi - ni. È
and tell her: 'Here is the seal to the pine-grove'." Ah, ha, the pine-grove! It's
ver ch'ei mi sog - giun - se; "guar - da che al - cun non ve - da." Ma
true, though, that he add - ed– "don't let a soul ob - serve you." But
Figaro
Barbarina
tu già ta - ce - ra - i. Si - cu - ra - men - te. A te già nien - te
you don't real - ly count. Why, of course not. It's none of your
Figaro
Barbarina
pre - me. Oh nien - te, nien - te. Ad - dio, mio bel cu -
bus - 'ness. In - deed not, it is - n't! It's high time that I

(Dances off.)
gi - no; vo da Su - san - na, e poi da Che - ru - bi - no.
hur - ried to see Su - san - na, and lat - er, Che - ru - bi - no.
Figaro (as if crushed)
Marcellina
Figaro
Marcellina
Ma - dre! Fi - glio! Son mor - to. Cal - ma - ti, fi - glio mi - o!
Moth - er! Yes, dear! This kills me! Don't get ex - cit - ed, son.
Figaro
Marcellina
Son mor - to, di - co. Flem - ma, flem - ma, e poi flem - ma: il fat - to è
This is out - ra - geous. Not so hast - y! think it o - ver. It is a
se - rio, e pen - sar - ci con - vien. Ma guar - da un po - co, che an - cor non
prob - lem, we must give it some thought. You must make sure that youre not the
Figaro
sai di chi si pren - da gio - co. Ah quel - la spil - la, o ma - dre, è quel - la
tar - get of some new de - cep - tion. But, dear - est moth - er, I tell you, that is the

Marcellina
stes - sa che poc' an - zi ei rac - col - se. È ver, ma que - sto al più ti por - ge un
pin for which the Count was look - ing. If so, that makes it all the more im -
drit - to di sta - re in guar - dia e vi - ve - re in so - spet - to; ma non
por - tant to act with cau - tion and fos - ter your least sus - pi - cion. Af - ter
Figaro
sai se in ef - fet - to— All' er - ta dun - que! il lo - co del con -
all, you do not know yet. But soon I will. I know the spot ex -
Marcellina
Figaro
gres - so so dov' è sta - bi - li - to. Do - ve vai, fi - glio mi - o? A ven - di -
act - ly they have set for their meet - ing. My dear son, where are you go - ing? To take re -
(Goes off furiously.)
car tut - t'i ma - ri - ti, ad - di - o.
venge for cheat - ed hus - bands, so help me!

Marcellina
Pre-sto av-ver-tiam Su-san-na. Io la cre-do in-no-cen-te. Quel-la
Quick-ly, I'll warn Su-san-na, I be-lieve she is guilt-less, she looks
fac-cia! quell' a-ria di mo-de-stia... è ca-so an-co-ra ch'el-la non
hon-est and sure-ly true to Fi-ga-ro... and if by chance I should be mis-
fos-se... ah, quan-do il cor non ciur-ma per-so-na-le in-te-
tak-en... now that I am her moth-er and no long-er her
res-se, o-gni don-na è por-ta-ta a la di-fe-sa del suo
ri-val, as a wo-man I am bound to be-come a de-fend-er of the
po-ve-ro ses-so, da quest' uo-mi-ni in-gra-ti a tor-to op-pres-so.
whole fe-male sex; for all men are un-grate-ful and should be pun-ished.

No. 24. Il capro e la capretta

The birds and beasts

Aria

Marcellina

let - ta la guer - ra mai non fa. Le più fe - ro - ci
sta - ble will nev - er fight their mares. A goose will find her
bel - ve per sel - ve e per cam - pa - gne la - scian le lor com -
gan - der a friend - ly good com - pan - ion, nev - er will he phi -
f
p
f
p
pa - gne in pa - ce e li - ber - tà, la - scian le lor com -
lan - der or wan - der ver - y far, nev - er will he phi -
pa - gne in pa - ce e li - ber - tà,
lan - der or wan - der ver - y far,

in li - ber -
or wan-der ver - y
tà. Il ca-pro e la ca- pret - ta son sem - pre in a - mi -
far. The roost - er loves each feath - er of his be - lov - ed
stà, l'a - gnel - lo all' a - gnel - let - ta la
hen; the li - on and his cho - sen li - on-ess are
guer - ra mai non fa. Le più fe - ro - ci
hap - py in their den. The most fer - o - cious

bel - ve per sel - ve e per cam - pa - gne
crea - tures have some re - deem - ing fea - tures —
sf
sf
la - scian le lor com - pa - gne in pa - ce e li - ber - tà, in li - ber -
But when it comes to man - kind that's some - thing else a - gain, something else a -
sf
Allegro
tà. Sol noi po - ve - re fem - mi - ne, che tan - to a - miam quest'
gain. We mem - bers of the fe - male sex are vic - tims of the
p
p
uo - mi - ni, trat - ta - te siam dai per - fi - di o - gnor con cru - del -
men we love. For all his faults and shameless ways the wo - man al - ways

tà, o - gnor con cru - del - tà; sol
pays, the wo - man al - ways pays. We
tr
p
f
noi po - ve - re fem-mi-ne, che tan-to a - miam quest' uo-mi-ni, che
tol - er - ate their jeal-ous-y, we of - fer them fi - del - i - ty, we
tan - to a - miam
love with lav - - - -
quest' uo-mi-ni, trat-ta - te siam dai per - fi - di o -
- - ish gen - er - os - i - ty. They pay us back with mis - er - y, and
cresc.

gnor con cru - del - tà, trat - ta - te siam dai per - fi - di o -
break our ten - der hearts, they pay us back with mis - er - y, and
gnor con cru-del - tà, con cru-del - tà,
break our ten-der hearts, they break our hearts,
con cru-del - tà, con cru - del - tà, con cru - del - tà.
they break our hearts, they break our hearts, they break our hearts.

Recitative

Barbarina, Figaro, Basilio, and Bartolo

Scene: *A thickly grown garden with two parallel pavilions)*

gno - ri." "Già lo sap - piam," eb - be - ne!
per - son." "That's what I thought." The mi - sers!
il pa - dron l'o - dia; ed io gli vo - glio be - ne, pe -
The Count can't stand him, but I, I love him dear - ly. A
rò co - stom - mi un ba - cio, e co - sa im - por - ta, for - se qual -
kiss is what it cost me... it does not mat - ter, I'll get it
(Frightened, she enters the pavilion on the left.)
(Enter Figaro in a cloak,
Figaro
cun me'l ren - de - rà. Son mor - ta! È Bar - ba -
back ver - y soon. Good gra - cious! It's Bar - ba -
and carrying a lantern. Then Basilio, Bartolo, a group of workmen, etc.)
Basilio
ri - na! Chi va là? Son quel - li che in - vi - ta - sti a ve -
ri - na! Who is there? Re - mem - ber, you have asked us to

Bartolo
nir. Che brut-to cef - fo! sem-bri un co-spi - ra - tor? Che dia-min
come. You look so sav - age, read - y to cut our throats. What is the
so - no que-gli in - fau - sti ap - pa - ra - ti? Lo ve-dre - te tra po - co.
point of these in - fer - nal prep - a - ra - tions? Ver - y soon you shall know it.
Figaro
In que-sto stes-so lo - co ce - le - bre - rem la fe - sta del - la mia spo-sa o -
You are a-bout to wit-ness the un - an - nounced re - vi - val of an old Span-ish
ne - sta e del feu - dal si - gnor. (Ah buo - no,
cus - tom by the Count and my bride. (Oh, charm-ing,
Basilio
buo - no, ca - pi - sco co - me e - gli è, ac - cor -
charm - ing! I see the light of day. They ar -

Figaro
da - ti si son sen-za di me.) Voi da que - sti con-tor - ni non vi sco -
ranged this af-fair with-out my help.) Stand where no one can see you — and watch what
sta - te, in - tan-to io va-do a dar cer - ti or - di - ni, e tor - no in po - chi i -
hap-pens. I'll give a few last - min - ute or - ders, but I'll re - turn here
(All exeunt except Bartolo and Basilio.)
stan - ti, a un fi - schio mi - o cor - re - te tut - ti quan - ti.
short - ly, and when I whis - tle, rush for - ward and sur - prise them.
Basilio
Bartolo
Basilio
Hai dia - vo - li nel cor - po! Ma co - sa quan - ti? Nul - la;
He's act - ing like a mad - man. Can you ex - plain it? Glad - ly:
Su - san - na pia-ce al Con - te; el - la d'ac - cor - do gli diè un ap - pun - ta -
the Count loves Su - san - na; she is pleased to ac - cord him an ap -

Bartolo
men-to ch'a Fi - ga-ro non pia-ce. E che? dun-que do-vria sof-frir-lo in
point-ment, and Fi-ga-ro is dis-pleased. Well, and? Is he sup-posed to take it
Basilio
pa-ce? Quel che sof - fro-no tan-ti, ei sof-frir non po -
calm-ly? Why should he be ex - empt-ed from what so man - y have
treb-be? e poi sen-ti-te che gua - da - gno può far? Nel mon-do, a -
suf-fered? And then, I ask you, what on earth could he gain? One learns one's
mi-co, l'ac-coz-zar-la con gran-di, fu pe-ri - co-lo o -
les - son. In this life, dear-est doc-tor, one must be re-al -
gno-ra, dan no - van - ta per cen-to e han vin-to an-co-ra.
is - tic. You can't eat your cake and al - so have it.

No. 25. In quegli anni

Youth is headstrong

Aria

Basilio

paz - zo, ch'or non son, fui quel paz - zo, ch'or non son. Ma col
just as big a fool, I was just as big a fool. But the
tr
tem-po e coi pe - ri - gli, Don-na Flem-ma ca - pi - tò; e i ca -
pass-ing years have brought me sense e-nough to swal-low pride; and ex -
pric - ci ed i pun - ti - gli dal - la te - sta mi ca -
per - ience at last has taught me not to swim a - gainst the
vò, dal - la te - sta mi ca - vò.
tide, not to swim a - gainst the tide.

Pres-so un pic-cio-lo a - bi - tu - ro,
Once, while I was on a jour-ney,
se - co lei mi tras-se un
I met Fa-ther Time in
gior - no, e to - glien - do giù dal mu - ro del pa - ci - fi - co sog -
per - son. In his hand he held an ob - ject which he of - fered me as
cresc.
p
cresc.
gior - no u - na pel - le di so - ma - ro, di so - ma - ro, di so -
pres - ent. 'Twas the hide__ of a don - key, of a don - key, of a
p
cresc.
p
cresc.
f
ma - ro. Pren - di, dis - se, o fi - glio ca - ro,
don - key. "Son," he said, "take this and wear it,
p

o fi - glio ca - ro!
you won't re - gret it!"
Poi di - spar-ve,e mi la -
Then he dis - ap-peared in
sciò,
air,
poi di - spar-ve,e mi la - sciò.
left me speech-less stand-ing there.
Tempo di Minuetto
Men-tre an - cor ta - ci - to guar - do quel do - no,
While I was lost in a - maze-ment and won - der,
p
men-tre an-cor guar - do quel do - no,
lost in a - maze-ment and won - der,
il ciel s'an -
a dread-ful
tr

nu - vo - la, rim - bom - ba il tuo - no, mi - sta al - la
storm a-rose. Thun - der was crash-ing, and like a
p
cresc.
f
gran - di - ne scro - scia la pio - va, scro - scia la pio - va.
wa - ter-fall the rain was splash - ing, and light-ning flash - ing.
Ec - co le mem - bra co - prir mi gio - va col man - to
I had no shel - ter, coat or um - brel - la. On - ly the
sf
d'a - si - no, che mi do - nò, col man - to d'a - si - no,
don-key hide lay there near-by. I slipped it o - ver me,

che mi do - nò. Fi - ni-sce il tur - bi - ne, io fo due pas - si.
it kept me dry. The sun came out a-gain and I pro - ceed-ed.
f
sf
Che fie - ra or - ri - bi - le dian - zi a me_ fas - si;
A hor - rid an - i - mal came out_ of_ no - where;
p
f
tr
Già, già, mi toc - ca, l'in - gor - da
its mouth wide o - pen, a - bout to
boc - ca, già di_ di - fen-der-mi spe - me non ho,
eat me. I stood there, pet - ri - fied. What could I do?

spe - me non ho, spe - me non ho. Ma il fiu - to i -
My life was doomed, that much I knew. All of a
gno - bi - le del mio ve - sti - to, tol - se al - la bel - va
sud - den the beast turned and bolt - ed; smell - ing the don - key hide,
sì l'ap - pe - ti - to, che di - sprez - zan - do - mi, che di - sprez - zan - do - mi,
it was re - volt - ed. I smelled so hor - ri - ble, it lost its ap - pe - tite,
si rin - sel - vo, si rin - sel -
and ran a - way, and ran a -

Allegro
vò. Co-sì co-no-sce-re mi fè la
way. Take this ad-vice, my friend, and learn this
sor-te, ch'on-te, pe-ri-co-li, ver-go-gna, e mor-te,
les-son: mal-ice and cal-um-ny, in-jus-tice, dis-hon-or,
col cuo-jo d'a-si-no fug-gir si può, ch'on-ta, pe-
will nev-er pen-e-trate a don-key's hide. Mal-ice and
ri-co-li, ver-go-gna, e mor-te, col cuo-jo d'a-si-no fug-
cal-um-ny, in-jus-tice, dis-hon-or, will nev-er pen-e-trate a

gir si può, col cuo-jo d'a-si-no fug-gir si può, col cuo-jo
don-key's hide, will nev-er pen-e-trate a don-key's hide, will nev-er
f
p
f
d'a-si-no fug-gir si può, fug-gir si
pen-e-trate a don-key's hide, a don-key's
p
(Exeunt Basilio and Bartolo.)
può, fug-gir si può.
hide, a don-key's hide.
cresc.
f

No. 26. Tutto è disposto... Aprite un po' quegli occhi

It won't be long now... O fellow man, be smarter!

Recitative and Aria

Figaro

mia ce-ri-mo-nia ei go-de-va leg-gen-do; e nel ve-der-lo, io ri-
wed-ding pro-ces-sion, when the Count read her mes-sage, I was laugh-ing! I was
p
de - va di me sen-za sa-per-lo. O Su-san-na! Su-
laugh-ing at my-self, and did not know it! Oh, Su-san-na! Su-
f
san-na! quan-ta pe-na mi co-sti! con quell' in-ge-nua fac-cia,
san-na, what de-spair you have caused me! Who would have thought you faith-less!
p
f
p
con que-gli oc-chi in-no-cen-ti, chi cre-du-to l'a-vri-a?
You were al-ways so hon-est, so na-ive and so win-ning!
f

Ah! che il fi-dar-si a don-na, a don-na, è o-gnor fol-li-a.
Ah, to put faith in wo-man, in wo-man, fool-ish be-gin-ning!
[Andante]
A-pri-te un po' quegl' oc-chi, uo-mi-ni in-cau-ti e
O fel-low man, be smart-er! Don't be a blind-ed
shioc-chi. Guar-da-te que-ste fem-mi-ne, guar-da-te co-sa
mar-tyr. Wake up and look at wo-men-folk and see them as they
son, guar-da-te co-sa son, guar-da-te, guar-da-te co-sa
are, and see them as they are, and see them as they real-ly
p
fp
sfp

son! Que - ste chia-ma - te De - e, da - gli in-gan - na - ti
are. Though you may call them an-gels, and like a slave a -
f
p
tr
sen - si, a cui tri - bu - ta in - cen - si la
dore them, your love will mere - ly bore them, but
de - bo - le ra - gion, la de - bo - le ra - gion, la
you will bear the scar, but you will bear the scar, but
de - bo - le ra - gion. Son stre - ghe che in -
you will bear the scar. Like witch - es with

can - ta - no per far - ci pe - nar, si - re - ne che
sor - cer - y, they charm and de - coy. Like si - rens with
tr
can - ta - no per far - ci af - fo - gar, ci - vet - te che al -
treach - er - y, they sing and de - stroy. They flat - ter their
tr
let - ta - no per trar - ci le piu - me, co - me - te che
van - i - ty and ca - ter to fash - ion, they cause us un -
bril - là - no per to - glier - ci il - lu - me, son ro - se spi -
hap - pi - ness and show no com - pas - sion. Like ros - es with
tr
sf
p

no - se, son vol - pi vez - zo - se, son or - se be -
bri - ars, like soft - spo - ken li - ars, ap - pear - ing de -
ni - gne, co - lom - be ma - li - gne, ma - e - stre d'in - gan - ni, a - mi - che d'af -
light - ful, yet vi - cious and spite - ful, their deal - ings are doub - le, they get us in
fan - ni, che fin - go - no, men - to - no, a - mo - re non sen - ton, non sen - ton pie -
troub - le de - ceit - ful and jeal - ous, to love they are cal - lous, their heart is of
tà, non sen - ton pie - tà, no, no, no, no. Il
stone, their heart is of stone, yes, made of stone! The
sf
p
cresc.
f
tr

re - sto, il re - sto nol di - co, già o - gnu-no,già o-gnu-no lo sa.
rest I need hard-ly to tell _ you, all that is suf-fi-cient-ly known.
sfp
A - prit-e un po' quegl' oc - chi, uo - mi-ni in-cau - ti e
Why don't you men get smart - er! Don't be a blind-ed
cresc.
fp
scioc-chi. Guar - da - te que - ste fem - mi-ne, guar-da - te co - sa
mar-tyr. Wake up and look at wo - men-folk and see them as they
son, co - sa son, co - sa son. Son stre - ghe che in - can - ta-no, il re - sto nol
are, as they are, as they are. Like witch - es they're haunt-ing us, what more need I
cresc.
f
p

di - co, si - re - ne che can - ta - no, il re - sto nol
tell you? Like si - rens they're taunt - ing us, what more need I
di - co, ci - vet - te che al - let - ta - no, il re - sto nol
tell you? They cause us un - hap - pi - ness, what more need I
di - co, co - me - te che bril - la - no, il re - sto nol
tell you? They flat - ter their van - i - ty, what more need I
di - co, son ro - se spi - no - se, son vol - pi vez -
tell you? Like ros - es with bri - ars, like soft - spo - ken
tr
tr
sf
p
sf
p

zo - se, son or - se be - ni - gne, co - lom - be ma -
li - ars, ap - pear - ing de - light - ful, yet vi - cious and
tr
sf
p
li - gne, ma - e - stre d'in - gan - ni, a - mi - che d'af - fan - ni, che fin - go - no,
spite - ful, their deal - ings are doub - le, they get us in troub - le, de - ceit - ful and
3
men - to - no, a - mo - re non sen - ton, non sen - ton pie -
jeal - ous, to love they are cal - lous, their heart is of
cresc.
tà, non sen - ton pie - tà, no, no, no, no. Il
stone, their heart is of stone, yes, made of stone! The
f

re - sto, il re - sto nol di - co, già o - gnu - no,già o-gnu - no lo sa, il
rest I need hard - ly to tell you, all that is suf-fi-cient-ly known, the
sfp
re - sto, il re-sto nol di - co, già o - gnu-no,già o-gnu-no lo sa,
rest I need hard-ly to tell you, all that is suf-fi-cient-ly known,
già o-gnu - no lo sa, già o-gnu - no lo sa, già o -
is all too well known, is all too well known, is
ff
(Retires.)
gnu - no lo sa.
all too well known!
f

Recitative

Susanna, Marcellina, Countess, and Figaro

Figaro (aside)
mi u - mi - da la not - te; io mi ri - ti - ro. (Ec - co - ci de la
night is damp and chil - ly. I'll go in - side now. (We are ar - riv - ing
Susanna
cri - si al gran - de i - stan - te.) Io sot - to que - ste pian - te, (se ma -
at the cru - cial mo - ment.) I'll stay a lit - tle long - er, if my
Figaro
da - ma il per - met - te), re-sto al pren - de - re il fre - sco u - na mezz' o - ra. Il fre - sco! il
la - dy will per - mit me; it is ear - ly and the night air is re - fresh - ing. Re - fresh - ing! Re -
Countess (Hides herself)
Susanna sotto voce
fre - sco! Re - sta - ci in buon' o - ra. (Il bir - bo è in sen - ti - nel - la, di - ver - tiam - ci an - che
fresh - ing! You have my per - mis - sion. (I know the rogue is spy - ing, it will give me much
no - i, dia - mo - gli la mer - cè de' dub - bi suo - i.)
plea - sure to re - im - burse him in full for his sus - pi - cions.)

No. 27. Giunse alfin il momento... Deh vieni, non tardar

This at last is the moment... Beloved, don't delay

Recitative and Aria

Susanna

sci - te dal mio pet - to, a tur - bar non ve - ni - te il mio di - let - to!
lov - ing arms em - brace me, and no wor - ry or fear shall mar our rap - ture!
tr
Oh co - me par che all' a - mo - ro - so
Close to the heart of Na - ture's friend - ly
tr
fo - co l'a - me - ni - tà del lo - co, la ter - ra e il ciel ri - spon - da,
pow - ers, del - i - cate, fra - grant flow - ers, the pine - trees, the sky sur - round us.
co - me la not - te i fur - ti miei se - con - da!
Aid - ing the lov - ers, night casts her veil a - round us!

[Andante]
p
Deh vie - ni, non tar - dar, o gio - ja bel - la.
Be - lov - ed, don't de - lay, the night is fall - ing.
Vie-ni o-ve a - mo - re per go - der t'ap - pel - la.
Has-ten where love's de - light is sweet - ly call - ing.
Fin - chè non splen - de in
Un - til the stars grow
ciel not - tur - na fa - ce,
pale, and night is wan - ing,
fin - chè l'a-ria è an-cor bru - na, e il mon - do
while the world is still and calm is

ta - ce. Qui mor - mo - ra il ru -
reign-ing. The brook-let rus - tles
scel, qui scher - za l'au - ra, che col dol - ce su - sur-ro il cor ri -
on,_ the breeze is blow - ing, and the tim-or-ous heart with hope is
stau - ra, qui ri - do - no i fio - ret - ti e l'er - ba è fre - sca,
glow - ing. The flow-ers all_with shin-ing dew_ are gleam-ing,
ai pia - ce - ri d'a - mor qui tut - to a - de - sca. Vie - ni, ben
while the world is long a - sleep and dream-ing. Come,_ my be -

mi - o, tra que - ste pian - te a - sco - se, vie - ni,
lov - ed, the star - ry sky a - bove you. Come, be -
vie - ni! Ti vo' la fron - te in - co - ro - nar di ro -
lov - ed! Come, my be - lov - ed, with all my heart, I love
colla voce
se, ti vo' la fron - te in - co - ro - nar, in - co - ro -
you. Come, my be - lov - ed, with all my heart, with all my
nar di ro - se.
heart I love you.
colla voce

Recitative

Figaro, Cherubino, and Countess

Finale of Act IV

No. 28. Pian, pianin le andrò più presso

On my tiptoes I'll go nearer

Cherubino, Countess, Count, Susanna, Figaro, Barbarina, Marcellina, Basilio, Bartolo, Antonio, and Don Curzio

net - ta! non ri - spon - de? Col - la ma - no il vol - to a -
san - na! Won't you an - swer? She pre - tends she does not
scon - de, or la bur - lo, or la bur - lo in ve - ri -
see me, but I'll show her that I know her lit - tle
(Takes her hand and caresses it.)
Countess (Trys to free herself; dis-
tà, or la bur - lo in ve - ri - tà. Ar - di - tel - lo! sfac - cia
game, pos - ing as a no - ble dame. Shame - less med - dler, don't come
guising her voice.)
Cherubino
tel - lo! i - te pre - sto via di quà! Smor -
near me, take your - self a - way from here! Su -
f
p
f
p
f
p

fio - sa, ma - li - zio - sa, io già
san - na, stop pre - tend - ing, I know
cresc.
Countess
Ar - di - tel - lo!
Who al - lowed you
so per - chè sei quà, smor -
well why you are here. You
sfac - cia - tel - lo! i - te pre - sto via di
to mo - lest me! Go at once a - way from
fio - sa, ma - li - zio - sa,
need-n't be con - de - scend - ing —

quà! sfac - cia - tel - lo! i - te
here! Shame - less med - dler! Go at
io già so per - chè sei quà, io già
You a - wait your cav - a - lier, and you
pre - sto via di quà! ar - di - tel - lo! sfac - cia -
once a - way from here! Who al - lowed you to mo -
so per - chè sei quà, io già
hope he'll soon be here! That's the
p
cresc.
tel - lo! i - te pre - sto via di quà! i - te pre - sto via di
lest me! Go at once a - way from here, go at once a - way from
so per - chè sei quà, io già so per - chè sei
rea - son why you're here, that's the rea - son you are
p
cresc.

quà!
here!
quà?
here!
Count (in the distance)
Ec - co quì la mia Su -
Here you are, my sweet Su -
f
p
3
sfp
Susanna (in the distance)
Ec - co quì l'uc - cel - la - to - re!
Here's our rov - ing Don Gio - van - ni!
Figaro (in the distance)
san - na! Ec - co quì l'uc - cel - la - to - re!
san - na! Here's our rov - ing Don Gio - van - ni!
Susanna
Ah! nel sen mi bat - te il
Ah! this shock came un - ex -
Cherubino
Non far me - co la ti - ran - na!
Don't act prud - ish and af - fect - ed!
Count
Ah! nel sen mi bat - te il
Ah! this shock came un - ex -
Figaro
Ah! nel sen mi bat - te il
Ah! this shock came un - ex -

co - re! Un altr' uom con lei si
pect - ed! There's a ri - val in his
Countess
Via, par - ti - te,o chia - mo gen - te!
Go, or I must call as - sis - tance!
Cherubino (keeping
Dam-mi un
Let me
co - re! Un altr' uom con lei si
pect - ed! There's a ri - val in my
co - re! Un altr' uom con lei si
pect - ed! There's a ri - val in his
sta; Al - la vo - ce è que-gli il
way. I am sure it's Che - ru -
An - che un
I should
her hand in his)
ba - cio, oh non fai nien - te;
kiss you, don't be so sil - ly.
sta; Al - la vo - ce è que-gli il
way. I am sure it's Che - ru -
sta; Al - la vo - ce è que-gli il
way. I am sure it's Che - ru -

(aside)
pag - gio,
bi - no.
te - me-ra - rio!
How of-fen - sive!
ba - cio! che co-rag - gio!
kiss you, what pre-sump - tion!
e per - chè_ far io non pos - so, quel che il
Why am I__ not once per - mit - ted what the
cresc.
f
p
te - me-ra - rio!
How in-sult - ing!
te - me-
What ef-
How in - sult - ing!
How of-fen - sive!
Con-te o-gnor fa - rà?
Count does ev - 'ry day?
oh! ve' che smor-fie!
Is it not time now
to stop pre-tend-ing?

ra - rio!
fron - t'ry!
te - me - ra - rio!
What pre - sump - tion!
oh! ve' che smor - fie! che
This ver - y morn - ing, re -
te - me - ra - rio! te - me -
His be - hav - ior is out -
te - me - ra - rio! te - me -
His be - hav - ior is out -
cresc.
(as above)
Se il ri - bal - do an - cor sta
If this ras - cal keeps in -
(as above)
Se il ri - bal - do an - cor sta
If this ras - cal keeps in -
smor - fie! Sai ch'io fui die - tro il so - fà.
mem - ber when I hid be - hind the chair?
(as above)
ra - rio!
ra - geous!
Se il ri - bal - do an - cor sta
If this ras - cal keeps in -
(as above)
ra - rio!
ra - geous!
Se il ri - bal - do an - cor sta
If this ras - cal keeps in -
f
p

sal - do, la fac - cen - da gua - ste - rà.
sist - ing, he will lead our plans a - stray.
sal - do, la fac - cen - da gua - ste - rà.
sist - ing, he will lead our plans a - stray.
(trying to kiss the Countess)
Pren - di in -
To be -
sal - do, la fac - cen - da gua - ste - rà.
sist - ing, he will lead our plans a - stray.
(The Count comes between the Countess and Cheru - bino, and receives the kiss.)
sal - do, la fac - cen - da gua - ste - rà.
sist - ing, he will lead our plans a - stray.
f
p
3
Countess
O cie - lo! il Con - te!
Good Lord, my hus - band!
Cherubino
(Joins Barbarina [in the pavilion])
tan - to! O cie - lo! il Con - te!
gin with... Good Lord, my mas - ter!
Figaro (drawing near to the Count)
Vo' ve - der co - sa fan
I must see what's go - ing
sfp

Count (Intending to give a box on the ear to Cherubino, he gives it to Figaro)
Per - chè voi non ri - pe - te - te, ri - ce - ve - te que - sto
Just to cool your youth - ful ar - dor, take this lit - tle gift from
là.
on.
Susanna (laughing)
Ah! ci ha
He is
Countess (laughing)
Ah! ci ha fat - to un bel gua -
That is just the prop - er
Count
(laughing)
quà.
me.
Ah! ci ha fat - to un bel gua -
That is just the prop - er
Figaro
Ah! ci ho fat - to un bel gua - da - gno,
This is pret - ty mea - ger pay - ment

fat - to un bel gua -
get - ting the prop - er
da - gno, col - la sua cu - rio - si -
treat - ment for the bold - ness he has
da - gno, col - la sua te - me - ri -
treat - ment for the bold - ness he has
col - la mia cu - rio - si - tà, ah! ci ho
for the in - t'rest I have shown, this is
cresc.
f
p
da - gno, ah! ci ha fat - to un bel gua - da - gno, col - la sua cu - rio - si -
treat - ment, he re - ceived the prop - er treat - ment for the en - vy he has
tà, ah! ci ha fat - to un bel gua - da - gno, col - la sua cu - rio - si -
shown; he re - ceived the prop - er treat - ment for the bold - ness he has
tà, ah! ci ha fat - to un bel gua - da - gno, col - la sua te - me - ri -
shown; he re - ceived the prop - er treat - ment for the bold - ness he has
fat - to un bel gua - da - gno, bel gua - da - gno, col - la mia cu - rio - si -
pret - ty mea - ger pay - ment for the in - t'rest, for the in - t'rest I have

f p
tà, ah! ah! ci ha
shown. Ah! Serves him
f p
tà, ah! ah! ci ha fat - to un bel gua -
shown. Ah! He has made me sim - ply
f p
tà, ah! ah! ci ha
shown. Ah! Ah! he
f p
tà, ah! ah! ci ho fat - to un bel gua -
shown. Ah! All I got for be - ing
f p
cresc. f p
fat - to un bel gua - da - gno, col - la sua cu - rio - si -
right for be - ing cu - rious, al - ways spy - ing on his
cresc. f p
da - gno, un bel gua - da - gno, col - la sua cu - rio - si -
fu - rious, sim - ply fu - rious, with his high and might - y
cresc. f p
fat - to un bel gua - da - gno, col - la sua te - me - ri -
made me sim - ply fu - rious with his high and might - y
cresc. p
da - gno, un bel gua - da - gno, col - la mia cu - rio - si -
cu - rious, be - ing cu - rious, is a bruised and ach - ing
cresc. f p

tà, ah! ci ha fat - to un bel gua - da - gno, col - la sua cu - rio - si -
own! May - be next time he'll know bet - ter, leav - ing well e - nough a -
tà, ah! ci ha fat - to un bel gua -
tone, may - be next time he'll know
tà, ah! ci ha fat - to un bel gua -
tone, may - be next time he'll know
tà, ah! ci ho fat - to
bone, ah, the next time
tà, ah! ci ha fat - to un bel gua - da - gno, col - la sua cu - rio - si -
lone, may - be next time he'll know bet - ter, leav - ing well e - nough a -
da - gno, col - la sua cu - rio - si -
bet - ter and leave well e - nough a -
da - gno, col - la sua te - me - ri -
bet - ter and leave well e - nough a -
un bel gua - da - gno, col - la
I shall know bet - ter and leave

tà, col-la sua cu-rio-si - tà, col-la sua cu-rio-si - tà!
lone, and leave well e-nough a-lone, and leave well e-nough a - lone!
tà, col - la sua cu - rio - si - tà!
lone, and leave well e - nough a - lone!
(Figaro retires.)
tà, te - me - ri - tà, te - me - ri - tà!
lone, he will leave well e - nough a - lone!
mia cu - rio - si - tà, cu - rio - si - tà!
well e - nough, leave well e - nough a - lone!
Con un poco più di moto
Count (to the Countess)
Par - ti - to è al - fin l'au -
At last no one dis -
da - ce,
turbs us.
ac - co - sta - ti, ben
Come o - ver here, my

Countess
mi - o! Giac - chè co - sì vi pia - ce, ec - co-mi qui, si -
dear - est! Your word is my com - mand-ment, here I am, my
tr
gnor!
lord!
Figaro
Che com - pia - cen - te fem - mi - na! Che spo - sa di buon
How will - ing and o - be - di - ent! She's al - ways in ac -
Count
Por - gi - mi la ma - ni - na.
Give me your hand, my dar - ling.
cor!
cord!

Countess
lo ve la do.
Here is my hand.
Count
Ca - ri - na!
I love you!
Count
Che di - ta te - ne -
What soft and love - ly
Figaro
Ca - ri - na?
He loves her?
rel - le! Che de - li - ca - ta pel - le! mi piz - zi - ca, mi
fin - gers! Their ten - der touch still lin - gers, it moves my heart to

Susanna
La
Such
Countess
La
Such
stuz-zi-ca, m'em - pie d'un nuo - vo ar - dor!
ec-sta-sy, rap - ture and joy com-bined!
Figaro
La cie - ca
Such wild in -
cie - ca pre-ven-zio - ne de -
wild in-fat-u-a - tion is
cie - ca pre-ven-zio-ne de -
wild in-fat-u-a-tion is
Che di-ta te-ne-rel - le!
What soft and love-ly fin - gers!
pre - ven - zio-ne de - lu - de
fat - u - a-tion is mere hal -

lu - de la ra - gio - ne, in -
mere hal - lu - ci - na - tion. It
lu - de la ra - gio - ne, in -
mere hal - lu - ci - na - tion. It
Che de - li - ca - ta pel - le!
Their ten - der touch still lin - gers,
la ra - gio - ne, in - gan - na i
lu - ci - na - tion. It blinds the
gan - na i sen - si o - gnor, in - gan - na i
blinds the hu - man mind, it blinds the
gan - na i sen - si o - gnor, in - gan - na i
blinds the hu - man mind, it blinds the
mi piz - zi - ca, mi stuz - zi - ca,
it moves my heart to ec - sta - sy,
sen - sio - gnor, in - gan - na i
hu - man mind, it blinds the
cresc.
f
p

sen - si, i sen - si o - gnor, i sen - si o -
fee - ble hu - man mind, the fee - ble
sen - si, i sen - si o - gnor, i sen - si o -
fee - ble hu - man mind, the fee - ble
m'em - pie d'un nuo - vo ar - dor, mi
rap - ture and joy com - bined, it
sen - si, i sen - si o - gnor, i sen - si o -
fee - ble hu - man mind, the fee - ble
cresc.
gnor, in - gan - na i sen - si, i sen - si o -
mind, it blinds the fee - ble hu - man
gnor, in - gan - na i sen - si, i sen - si o -
mind, it blinds the fee - ble hu - man
piz - zi - ca, mi stuz - zi - ca, m'em - pie d'un nuo - vo ar -
moves my heart to ec - sta - sy, rap - ture and joy com -
gnor, in - gan - na i sen - si, i sen - si o -
mind, it blinds the fee - ble hu - man
f p

gnor.
mind.
gnor.
mind.
Count
dor.
bined.
Ol - tre la do - te, o
Dar - ling, be-sides your
gnor.
mind.
cresc.
p
ca - ra! Ri - ce - vi an - co un bril - lan - te che a te por - ge un' a -
dow - ry, ac - cept this lit - tle pres - ent, a dia - mond ring as
Countess
Tut - to Su - san - na
(Gives the Countess a ring.) Glad - ly Su - san - na
man - te in pe - gno del suo a - mor.
to - ken of my un - dy - ing love.
cresc.
p

Susanna
Va tut - to a
Our plan is
pi - glia dal suo be - ne - fat - tor.
wel - comes her ben - e - fac - tor's gift.
Count
Va tut - to a
My plan is
Figaro
Va tut - to a
Our plan is
cresc.
ma - ra - vi - glia, ma il me - glio man - ca an -
fast pro - ceed - ing, the best is yet to
ma - ra - vi - glia, ma il me - glio man - ca an -
fast pro - ceed - ing, the best is yet to
ma - ra - vi - glia, ma il me - glio man - ca an -
fast pro - ceed - ing, the best is yet to
f
p

cor.
come.
Countess (to the Count)
Si - gnor, d'ac - ce - se fiac - co - le, io veg-gio il ba - le -
My lord, I see the glow of flam - ing torch - es in the
cor.
come.
cor.
come.
nar.
night.
Count
En - triam, mia bel - la Ve - ne - re, an - dia - mo - ci a ce -
Well, then, let us a - void them all and hur - ry out of

Susanna
Ma - ri - ti sci - mu - ni - ti, sci - mu - ni - ti, ve -
Come on, you fool - ish hus - bands, fool - ish hus - bands, it's
Count
lar! En - triam, mia bel - la Ve - ne - re,
sight! Well then, let us a - void them all,
Figaro
Ma - ri - ti sci - mu - ni - ti, ve - ni -
Come on, you fool - ish hus - bands, it's time
sf
p
sf
p
ni - te ad im - pa - rar, ad im - pa - rar!
time you saw the light, you saw the light!
Countess
Al bu - io, si - gnor mi - o?
You mean there in the dark?
an - dia - mo - ci a ce - lar! È quel - lo che vogl'
and hur - ry out of sight. What else would suit us
- te ad im - pa - rar!
you saw the light!

i - o, tu sai, che là per leg - ge - re, io non de - sio d'en -
bet - ter? I do not want to read to you in there, Su - san - na
sf
p
I fur - bi so - no in trap - po - la, co - min - cia ben l'af -
Our plan is work - ing splen - did - ly, now comes the best of
I fur - bi so - no in trap - po - la, co - min - cia ben l'af -
Figaro
Our plan is work - ing splen - did - ly, now comes the best of
trar. La perfida, lo se - gui - ta, è va - no il du - bi -
dear. She fol - lows ver - y will - ing - ly, there is no doubt at
far, co - min - cia ben l'af - far.
all, now comes the best of all.
far, co - min - cia ben l'af - far.
all, now comes the best of all.
Count (in a feigned voice)
Figaro
(in a rage)
(Figaro crosses the stage)
tar, è va - no il du - bi - tar.
all, there is no doubt at all.
Chi pas - sa?
Who goes there?
Pas - sa
Lots of
f

Countess
(Goes into the right pavilion)
Count
gen- te. È Fi - ga-ro! men vo! An - da-te,an-
peo-ple. It's Fi - ga-ro! I'll hide! You go a -
p
(Disappears among the bushes.)
da - te! io poi ver - rò.
head then! I'll meet you soon.
f
p
Larghetto
Figaro
Tut - to è tran-quil-lo e
Now all is still and
pla - ci-do, en - trò la bel- la
calm a-gain. The lov - ers meet in

Ve - ne-re; col va - go Mar-te, pren - de-re
se - cre-cy, but I shall guide their des - tin-y;
sf
nuo - vo Vul-can del se - co-lo, in re - te la po -
bid - ing my time ju - di - cious-ly, to catch them both at
p
Allegro molto
Susanna (in a feigned voice)
Figaro
trò! Ehi Fi - ga-ro! ta - ce - te! Oh que - sta è la Con -
once! Ho, Fi - ga-ro! Be qui - et! Ah, that must be the
sfp
sfp
tes - sa! A tem - po quì giun - ge - te, ve -
Count-ess! Your com - ing here is time - ly. Ob -
cresc.
f
p

dre - te là voi stes - sa, il Con-te e la mia spo-sa, di
serve in what a man - ner your hus-band and my Su-san-na ar-
pro - pria man la co - sa toc - car io vi fa - rò, toc -
ranged a se-cret meet - ing. Just wait and you will see, just
sf
Susanna (forgetting to
car io vi fa - rò, toc - car io vi fa - rò. Par-la-te un po' più
wait and you will see, just wait and you will see. Be care-ful and speak
p
sf
p
change her voice)
bas - so, di quà non muo-vo il pas - so, ma ven - di-car - mi
soft - ly. I swear I will not leave here till I have had re -
sf
p

Figaro
vo', ma ven-di-car-mi vo'.
venge, till I have had re-venge!
(Su-
(Su-
sf
p
Susanna
Sì!
Yes!
san-na!)
san-na!)
Ven-di-car-si?
You want venge-ance?
(L'i-ni-quo io
(The trai-tor
Co-me, co-me po-tri-a far-si?
Venge-ance? May I be at your ser-vice?
f
p

vo' sor - pren-de-re, poi so quel che fa -
thinks he's fool-ing me, but he is ver - y
La vol-pe vuol sor - pren-der-mi, e
The vix-en thinks she's fool-ing me, so
f
rò, l'i-ni - quo io vo' sor-pren -
wrong. The trai - tor thinks he's fool -
se-con-dar-la vo', la vol - pe vuol sor-pren - der-mi, e
I will play a - long. The vix - en thinks she's fool - ing me, so
f
p
- de-re, poi sò quel che fa - rò, poi
- ing me, but he is ver - y wrong, but
p
se - con-dar-la vo', e se - con - dar, e
I will play a - long, I'll play a - long, so
p

so quel che fa - rò.)
he is ver - y wrong.)
(slyly joining the game)
se-con-dar-la - vo!
I will play a - long.
Ah, se ma - da - ma il
Count-ess, I am de -
Susanna (aside)
Figaro
vuo - le! Su via, man-co pa - ro - le! Ah, ma -
lir - ious. (What's this, can he be se - rious?) Ah, my
cresc.
fp
Susanna
Figaro (as above)
da - ma! Su via, man-co pa - ro - le. Ec - co-mi a'
la - dy! In - deed, he must be se - rious. I'm on my
cresc.
f
p
vo - stri pie - di, ho pie - no il cor di
knees be - fore you; you know that I a -
sfp

fo - co,
e - sa - mi - na - te il lo - co,
dore you,
re - mem - ber what you told me:
sf
p
Pen - sa - te al tra - di - tor!
You're here to take__ re - venge.
Susanna
(Co - me la man mi
(I__ hard-ly can re -
3
3
3
Figaro
Susanna
piz - zi - ca!)
strain my-self.)
(Co - me il pol - mon mi s'al - te - ra!)
(What a de - light - ful com - e - dy!)
(Che
(My
Figaro
sma - nia! che fu - ror!)
blood be - gins to boil!)
(Che sma - nia! che ca -
(Her blood be - gins to

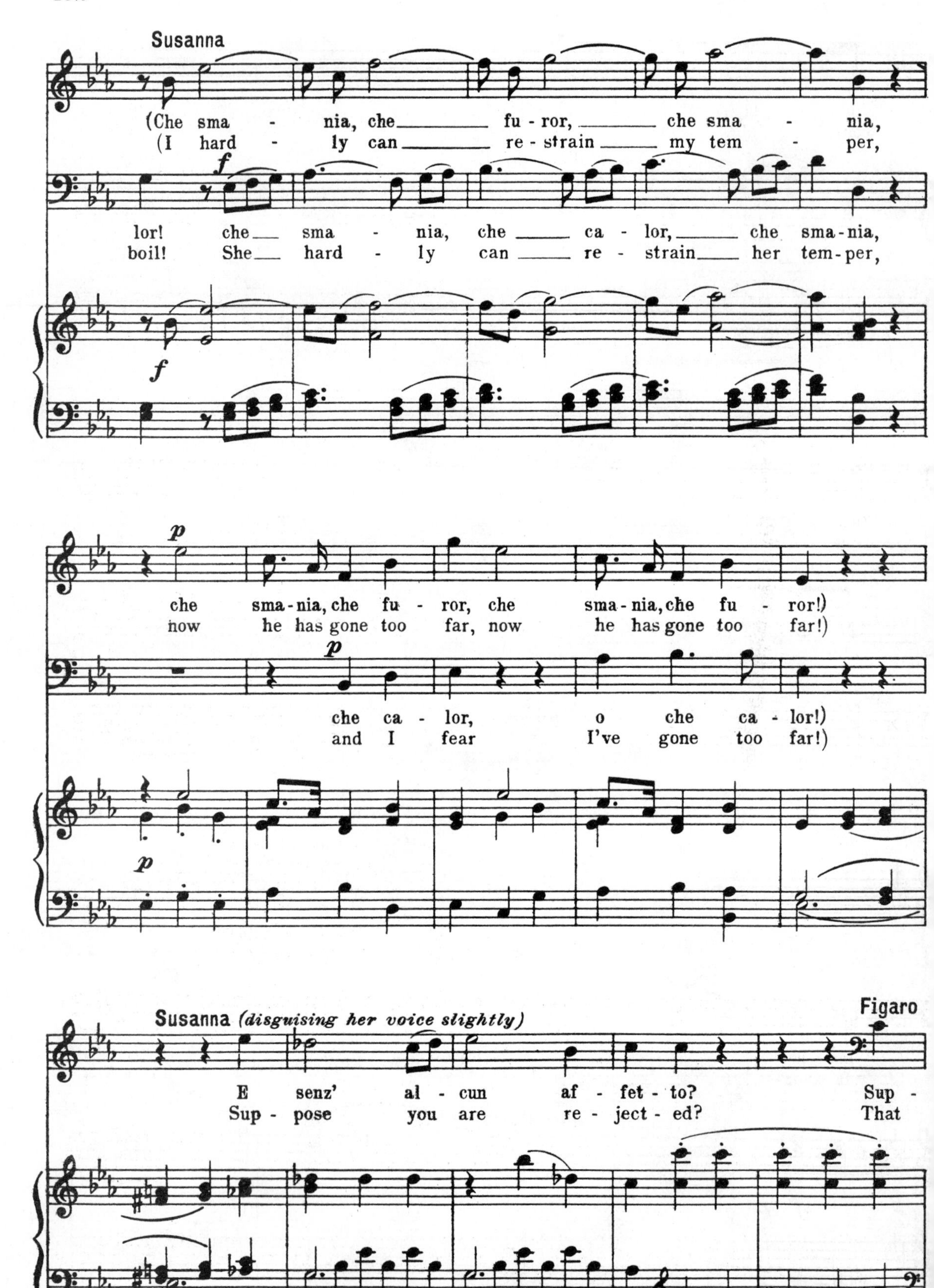
Susanna
(Che sma - nia, che fu - ror, che sma - nia,
(I hard - ly can re - strain my tem - per,
f
lor! che sma - nia, che ca - lor, che sma - nia,
boil! She hard - ly can re - strain her tem - per,
f
p
che sma - nia, che fu - ror, che sma - nia, che fu - ror!)
now he has gone too far, now he has gone too far!)
p
che ca - lor, o che ca - lor!)
and I fear I've gone too far!)
p
Susanna (disguising her voice slightly)
Figaro
E senz' al - cun af - fet - to? Sup -
Sup - pose you are re - ject - ed? That

pli - sca - vi il ri - spet - to! Non per - diam
would be un - ex - pect - ed! We can't lose
sf
p
(rubbing his hands)
tem - po in - va - no: Da - te - mi un po' la
time de - bat - ing, grant me some sign of
Susanna
(Resumes her natural voice, and boxes his ears.)
Ser - vi - te - vi, si - gnor!
Right here where it be - longs!
ma - no, da - te - mi un po' — Che
fa - vor — give me your hand. You
sf p

(Continues to box his ear
Che schiaf - fo! e que - sto,
Take this one! and this one,
schiaf - fo!
slapped me!
e an-co-ra que - sto, e que-sto e poi quest' al-tro, e
and still an-oth - er, and this one, and still an-oth-er, and
Non bat-ter co-sì
Don't hit so hard, I
que - sto, si-gnor scal - tro, e que - sto, e poi quest'al-tro an-
this, you schem-ing trai - tor, take this one, and still an-oth-er
pre - sto!
beg you!
cresc.
f

cor.
one.
Im - pa - ra, im-pa - ra, o
I'll teach you to be -
O
Oh,
schiaf - fi gra - zio - sis - si - mi,
pre - cious, wel - come pun - ish-ment
p
sfp
per - fi - do!
have your-self!
a fa - re il se - dut - tor,
and mind your own af - fairs!
o mio fe - li - ce a - mor,
from her be - lov - ed hand!
o
Oh,
sf
p
im - pa - ra, im - pa - ra a fa - re il
I warn you not to let it
schiaf - fi gra - zio - sis - si - mi,
pre - cious, wel - come pun - ish-ment
o mio fe -
from her be -

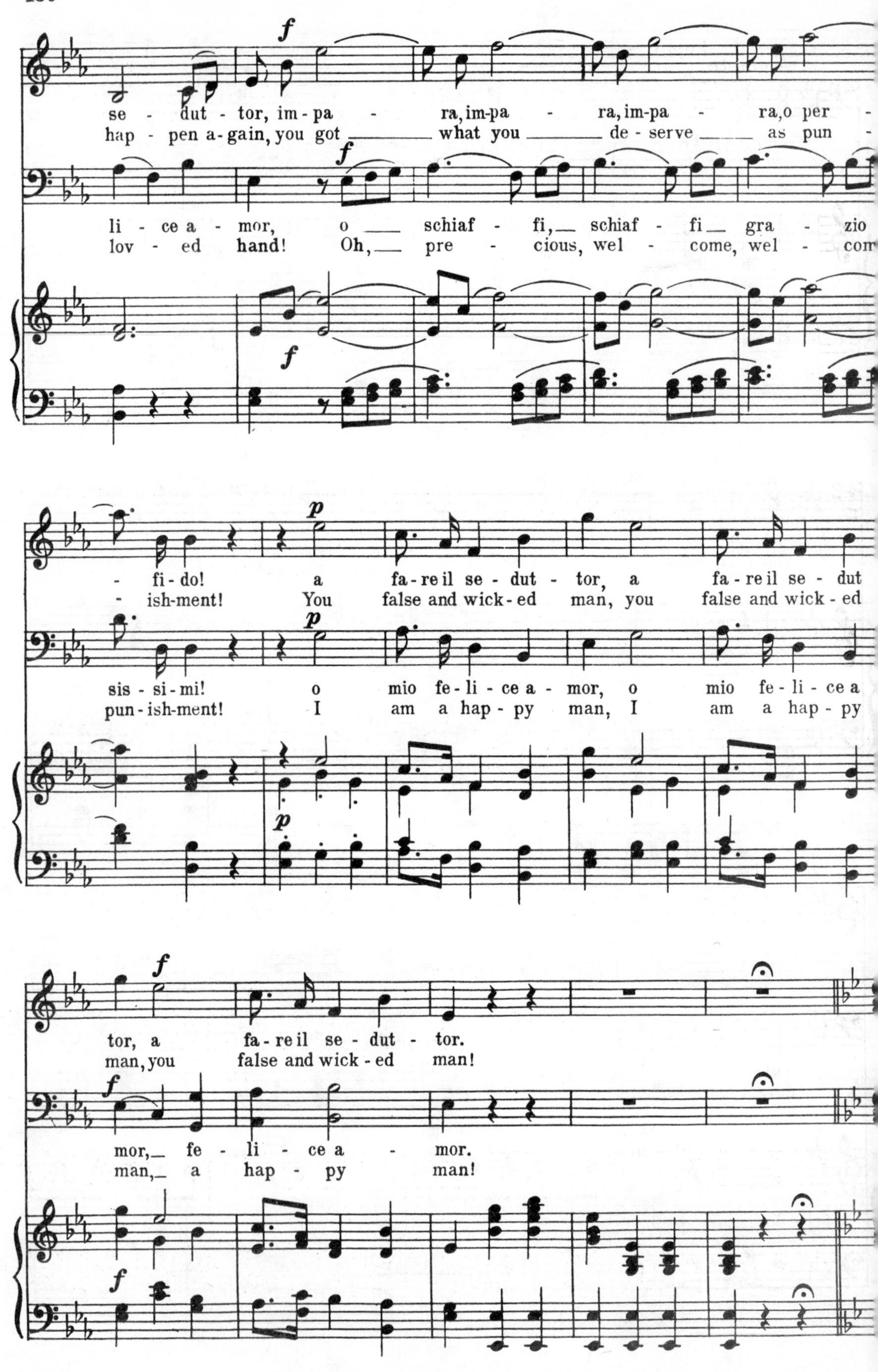
f
se - dut - tor, im-pa - ra, im-pa - ra, im-pa - ra, o per -
hap - pen a-gain, you got what you de - serve as pun -
f
li - ce a - mor, o schiaf - fi, schiaf - fi gra - zio
lov - ed hand! Oh, pre - cious, wel - come, wel - com
f
p
- fi - do! a fa - re il se - dut - tor, a fa - re il se - dut
- ish-ment! You false and wick - ed man, you false and wick - ed
p
sis - si - mi! o mio fe - li - ce a - mor, o mio fe - li - ce a
pun - ish-ment! I am a hap - py man, I am a hap - py
p
f
tor, a fa - re il se - dut - tor.
man, you false and wick - ed man!
f
mor, fe - li - ce a - mor.
man, a hap - py man!
f

Andante
Figaro (Kneels.)
Pa - ce, pa - ce, mio dol - ce te - so - ro! Io co -
My a - pol - o - gy, dar - ling, I owe you. From your
f
p
nob - bi la vo - ce che a - do - ro, e che im - pres - sa o-gnor ser - bo nel
voice it was eas - y to know you, from your sweet lit - tle voice I a -
Susanna (surprised and laughing)
La mia vo - ce?
From my voice?
cor.
dore!
La vo - ce che a -
How could I mis -

Pa - ce, pa - ce, mio dol - ce te - so - ro! pa - ce,
Dar - ling, dar - ling, I love and a - dore you, dear - est
do - ro! Pa - ce, pa - ce, mio dol - ce te - so - ro! pa - ce,
take it! Dar - ling, dar - ling, I love and a - dore you, dear - est
pa - ce, mio te - ne - ro a - mor! pa - ce, pa - ce, mio te - ne - ro a -
love, let us quar - rel no more, dear - est love, let us quar - rel no
pa - ce, mio te - ne - ro a - mor! pa - ce, pa - ce, mio te - ne - ro a -
love, let us quar - rel no more, dear - est love, let us quar - rel no
mor! pa - ce, pa - ce, mio te - ne - ro a - mor!
more, dear - est love, let us quar - rel no more!
Count (Enters.)
mor! pa - ce, pa - ce, mio te - ne - ro a - mor! Non la
more, dear - est love, let us quar - rel no more! Where she

Susanna
Que - sti è il Con - te, al - la vo - ce il co -
That's the voice of the frus - tra - ted
Figaro
tro - vo e gi - rai tut - to il bo - sco! Que - sti è il Con - te, al - la vo - ce il co -
is I can - not dis - cov - er! That's the voice of the frus - tra - ted
no - sco.
lov - er.
(Turns toward the pavilion in which the Countess has hidden, and opens it.)
Bel - la,
Splen - did,
Count
no - sco. Ehi, Su - san - na! sei sor - da? sei mu - ta?
lov - er. Ho, Su - san - na! Can't you hear me? Where are you?
f
bel - la! non l'ha co - no - sciu - ta. Ma - da - ma!
splen - did, he still does not know her! My la - dy!
Figaro
Chi? Ma -
Who? The
p

Ma - da - ma! La com - me-dia, i - dol mio, ter - mi -
The Count - ess! Now to bring the bur-lesque to an
da - ma? La com - me-dia, i - dol mio, ter - mi -
Count-ess? Now to bring the bur-lesque to an
nia - mo, con - so - lia-mo il biz-zar-ro a - ma - tor, con - so -
end - ing, we must e - ven the score with the Count, we ___ must
nia - mo, con - so - lia-mo il biz-zar-ro a - ma - tor, con - so -
end - ing, we must e - ven the score with the Count, we ___ must
lia-mo il biz-zar-ro a - ma - tor, con - so - lia-mo il biz-zar-ro a - ma -
e - ven the score with the Count, we ___ must e - ven the score with the
lia-mo il biz-zar-ro a - ma - tor, con - so - lia-mo il biz-zar-ro a - ma -
e - ven the score with the Count, we ___ must e - ven the score with the

Count
tor.
La mia
Count.
(Falls at Susanna's feet.)
It's the
tr
tor.
Sì, ma - da - ma, voi sie - te il ben
Count.
Ah, my lady, I love you so
tr
spo - sa? ah! senz' ar - me son i - o!
Count-ess! Ah, and I have no weap-ons!
mi - o! Un ri - sto - ro al mio
mad - ly! Won't you fa - vor my
cresc.
f
p
Susanna
Io son quì, fac-cio quel che vo - le - te.
I am read-y and at your dis-po - sal!
Count
cor con - ce - de - te? Ah, ri -
lov - ing pro - po - sal? Ah, be -
f

Susanna
Ah, cor-ria-mo, cor-ria-mo, mio be-ne, e le
Let us hur-ry a-way and be hap-py, let us
Figaro
bal-di! ri-bal-di! Ah, cor-ria-mo, cor-ria-mo, mio be-ne, e le
tray-ers, be-tray-ers! Let us hur-ry a-way and be hap-py, let us
pe-ne com-pen-si il pia-cer, e le pe-ne com-pen-si il pia-
bur-y our troub-les in joy, let us bur-y our troub-les in
pe-ne com-pen-si il pia-cer, e le pe-ne com-pen-si il pia-
bur-y our troub-les in joy, let us bur-y our troub-les in
(Susanna enters the pavilion on the left.)
cer, e le pe-ne com-pen-si il pia-cer.
joy, let us bur-y our troub-les in joy.
cer, e le pe-ne com-pen-si il pia-cer.
joy, let us bur-y our troub-les in joy.

Allegro assai
Count
Figaro (pretending great fear)
Gen - te, gen-te! all' ar-mi, all' ar - mi! Il pa -
Hur - ry, hur - ry, come with weap-ons! That's my
f
p
(Enter Bartolo, Basilio, Don Curzio, Antonio, and servants with torches.)
Count
Figaro
dro - ne! Gen - te! gen-te! a - ju - to! a - ju - to! Son per -
mas - ter! Guards and ser - vants, come and help me! I'm out -
Basilio and Don Curzio
Cos' av - ven - ne? cos' av - ven - ne?
What has hap-pened, what has hap-pened?
Antonio and Bartolo
Count
du - to! Cos' av - ven - ne? cos' av - ven - ne? Il scel - le -
num-bered! What has hap-pened, what has hap-pened? This wretch-ed
sf
p

ra - to m'ha tra - di - to, m'ha in-fa - ma - to, e con chi sta-te a ve - der!
scoun-drel has be-trayed me, act - ed base - ly, and with whom you soon shall see!
Basilio and Don Curzio sotto voce
Son stor - di - to, sba - lor - di - to! Non mi
I am speech-less and be - wil - dered! Can it
Antonio and Bartolo sotto voce
Son stor - di - to, sba - lor - di - to! Non mi
I am speech-less and be - wil - dered! Can it
Figaro sotto voce
Son stor - di - ti, sba - lor - di - ti!
They are speech-less and be - wil - dered!
par che ciò sia ver!
be that this is true?
par che ciò sia ver!
be that this is true?
Count
O che sce - na, che pia - cer! In - van re - si -
They can - not be - lieve it's true! There's no use re -

ste - te, u - sci - te, ma - da - ma! Il pre - mio or a -
sist - ing, in - sist - ing on hid - ing. Come out now, my
f
p
cresc.
sf
p
(The Count reaches into the left pa-
vre - te, di vo - stra o - ne - stà! Il
Count - ess, and get your re - ward! Che - ru -
tr
sf
p
sf
sf
p
lion and pulls out a resisting Cherubino,
en Barbarina, Marcellina, and Susanna.)
Antonio
Figaro
pag - gio! Mia fi - glia! Mia
bi - no! My daugh - ter! My
tr
Basilio and Don Curzio
Ma - da - ma!
My la - dy!
Antonio
Ma - da - ma!
My la - dy!
Bartolo
Count
ma - dre! Ma - da - ma! Sco - per - ta è la
moth - er! My la - dy! Your plot is dis -
tr
cresc.
sf
p

tra - ma, la per - fi - da è quà, la per - fi - da è
cov - ered, most faith - less of wives, so false to her
sf p sf p cresc.
Susanna (Kneels before the Count, holding her handkerchief before her face.)
Count
Per - do - no, per - do - no! No, non sp
For - give me, for - give me! No, nev - e
quà!
lord!
p f
rar - lo!
nev - er!
No, no, non vo'
There's no chance what
Figaro (Kneels.)
Per - do - no, per - do - no!
For - give her, for - give her!
p f

Susanna
cresc.
Per - do - no! per - do - no!
For - give me! for - give me!
Cher., Barb. and Marc. (All kneel.)
Per - do - no! per - do - no!
For - give her! for - give her!
Basilio and Don Cur. (All kneel.)
Per - do - no! per - do - no!
For - give her! for - give her!
Count
dar - lo! no!
ev - er! no!
Fig., Bart. and Ant. (All kneel.)
Per - do - no! per - do - no!
For - give her! for - give her!
per - do - no!
for - give me!
per - do - no!
for - give her!
Countess
per - do - no!
for - give her!
Al -
I
Count (more forcefully)
no! No, no, no, no, no, no!
no! No, no, no, no, no, no!
per - do - no!
for - give her!

(Comes out of the other pavilion and is about to kneel when the Count prevents her.)
me - no per lo - ro, per - do - no ot - ter - rò!
know you'll for - give them, for my sake at least!
pp
Basilio and Don Curzio sotto voce
O cie - lo! che
I can - not con -
Count sotto voce
O cie - lo! che
I can - not con -
Antonio and Bartolo sotto voce
O cie - lo! che
I can - not con -
sempre stacc.
pp
veg - gio! de - li - ro! va
ceive it, I scarce - ly be
veg - gio! de - li - ro! va
ceive it, I scarce - ly be
veg - gio! de - li - ro! va
ceive it, I scarce - ly be

neg - gio! Che cre - der, che
lieve it, I hard - ly can
neg - gio! Che cre - der, che
lieve it, I hard - ly can
neg - gio! Che cre - der, che
lieve it, I hard - ly can
cre - der non sò, non
cred - it my eyes! What's
cre - der non so, non
cred - it my eyes! What's
cre - der non so, non
cred - it my eyes! What's
p

Andante
so, non so.
this I see?
so, non so.
this I see?
Count (supplicatingly)
so, non so. Con - tes - sa, per -
this I see? My_ la - dy, for -
Andante
p
Countess
do - no! per - do - no, per - do - no! Più do - ci - le io
give me, be - lov - ed, for - give me! How could I re -
so - no, e di - co di sì,_ e di - co di
fuse it, my heart speaks for you,_ my heart_speaks for

Susanna and Countess sotto voce
sì. Ah tut - ti con - ten - ti sa - re - mo co - sì, sa - re - mo co - sì, ah tut - ti con - ten - ti sa - re - mo co -
you. We all are con - tent - ed and hap - py a - gain, and hap - py a - gain, we all are con - tent - ed and hap - py a -
Cher. Barb. and Marc. sotto voce
Ah tut - ti con - ten - ti sa - re - mo co - sì, sa - re - mo co - sì, ah tut - ti con - ten - ti sa - re - mo co -
We all are con - tent - ed and hap - py a - gain, and hap - py a - gain, we all are con - tent - ed and hap - py a -
Basilio and Don Curzio sotto voce
Ah tut - ti con - ten - ti sa - re - mo co - sì, sa - re - mo co - sì, ah tut - ti con - ten - ti sa - re - mo co -
We all are con - tent - ed and hap - py a - gain, and hap - py a - gain, we all are con - tent - ed and hap - py a -
Count sotto voce
Ah tut - ti con - ten - ti sa - re - mo co - sì, sa - re - mo co - sì, ah tut - ti con - ten - ti sa - re - mo co -
We all are con - tent - ed and hap - py a - gain, and hap - py a - gain, we all are con - tent - ed and hap - py a -
Ant. Bart. and Fig. sotto voce
Ah tut - ti con - ten - ti sa - re - mo co - sì, sa - re - mo co - sì, ah tut - ti con - ten - ti sa - re - mo co -
We all are con - tent - ed and hap - py a - gain, and hap - py a - gain, we all are con - tent - ed and hap - py a -
cresc.
p
dim.

sì, ah tut - ti con - ten - ti sa - re -
gain, we all are con - tent - ed and hap -
sì, ah tut - ti con - ten - ti sa -
gain, we all are con - tent - ed and
sì, ah tut - ti con - ten - ti sa -
gain, we all are con - tent - ed and
sì, ah tut - ti con - ten - ti sa -
gain, we all are con - tent - ed and
sì, ah tut - ti con - ten - ti sa -
gain, we all are con - tent - ed and
- mo, sa - re - mo co - sì.
- py, and hap - py a - gain.
re - mo, sa - re - mo co - sì.
hap - py, and hap - py a - gain.
re - mo, sa - re - mo co - sì.
hap - py, and hap - py a - gain.
re - mo, sa - re - mo co - sì.
hap - py, and hap - py a - gain.
re - mo, sa - re - mo co - sì.
hap - py, and hap - py a - gain.

Allegro assai
Que - sto gior - no di tor -
All day long we were tor -
men - ti, di ca - pric - cie di fol -
ment - ed, an - gry, fool - ish, and ex -
Allegro assai

li - a, In con - ten-ti e in al - le - gri - a, So-lo a - mor può ter - mi -
cit - ed, but at last we are u - nit - ed by the mag - ic force of
li - a, In con - ten-ti e in al - le - gri - a, So-lo a - mor può ter - mi -
cit - ed, but at last we are u - nit - ed by the mag - ic force of
li - a, In con - ten-ti e in al - le - gri - a, So-lo a -
cit - ed, but at last we are u - nit - ed by the
li - a, In con - ten-ti e in al - le - gri - a, So-lo a -
cit - ed, but at last we are u - nit - ed by the
li - a, In con - ten-ti e in al - le - gri - a, So-lo a -
cit - ed, but at last we are u - nit - ed by the
p
f
p
sf
f
nar, so - lo a - mor può ter - mi -
love, by the mag - ic force of
nar, so - lo a - mor può ter - mi -
love, by the mag - ic force of
mor può ter - mi - nar, so - lo a - mor può ter - mi -
mag - ic force of love, by the mag - ic force of
mor può ter - mi - nar, so - lo a - mor può ter - mi -
mag - ic force of love, by the mag - ic force of
mor può ter - mi - nar, so - lo a - mor può ter - mi -
mag - ic force of love, by the mag - ic force of
f
sf

nar. Spo - si! a - mi - ci! al bal - lo! al
love. Lov-ers and coup-les, with laugh-ter and
nar. Spo - si! a - mi - ci! al bal - lo! al
love. Lov-ers and coup-les, with laugh-ter and
nar. Spo - si! a - mi - ci! al bal - lo! al
love. Lov-ers and coup-les, with laugh-ter and
nar. Spo - si! a - mi - ci! al bal - lo! al
love. Lov-ers and coup-les, with laugh-ter and
nar. Spo - si! a - mi - ci! al bal - lo! al
love. Lov-ers and coup-les, with laugh-ter and
gio - co! Al - le mi - ne da - te fo - co, da - te fo - co!
sing - ing, let the wed - ding bells chime in with joy - ous ring - ing!
gio - co! Al - le mi - ne da - te fo - co, da - te fo - co!
sing - ing, let the wed - ding bells chime in with joy - ous ring - ing!
gio - co! Al - le mi - ne da - te fo - co, da - te fo - co!
sing - ing, let the wed - ding bells chime in with joy - ous ring - ing!
gio - co! Al - le mi - ne da - te fo - co, da - te fo - co!
sing - ing, let the wed - ding bells chime in with joy - ous ring - ing!
gio - co! Al - le mi - ne da - te fo - co, da - te fo - co!
sing - ing, let the wed - ding bells chime in with joy - ous ring - ing!

Ed al suon di lie - ta mar - cia,
And to joy - ous strains of mu - sic,
Ed al suon di lie - ta mar - cia,
And to joy - ous strains of mu - sic,
Ed al suon di lie - ta mar - cia,
And to joy - ous strains of mu - sic,
Ed al suon, al suon di lie - ta
And to joy - ous strains of rous - ing
Ed al suon di lie - ta mar - cia,
And to joy - ous strains of mu - sic,

cor - riam tut - ti a fe - steg - giar,
sing and dance till break of day,
cor - riam tut - ti a fe - steg - giar,
sing and dance till break of day,
cor - riam tut - ti a fe - steg-giar,
sing and dance till break of day,
mar - cia, cor - riam tut - ti, tut - ti a fe - steg -
mu - sic, let's make mer - ry, till the break of
cor - riam tut - ti a fe - steg - giar,
sing and dance till break of day,
f
cor - riam tut - ti a fe - steg - giar.
sing and dance till break of day.
f
cor - riam tut - ti a fe - steg - giar.
sing and dance till break of day.
f
cor - riam tut - ti a fe - steg - giar.
sing and dance till break of day.
f
giar, cor - riam tut - ti a fe - steg - giar.
day, sing and dance till break of day.
f
cor - riam tut - ti a fe - steg - giar.
sing and dance till break of day.
f
p

p
cresc.
Cor-riam tut-ti, cor-riam
Let's make mer-ry, let's make
Cor-riam tut-ti, cor-riam tut-ti,
Let's make mer-ry, let's make mer-ry,
f
tut-ti, cor-riam tut-ti, cor-riam tut-ti, cor-riam tut - ti a
mer-ry, and to joy-ous strains of mu-sic, sing and dance till
cor-riam tut-ti, cor-riam tut-ti, cor-riam tut - ti a
and to joy-ous strains of mu-sic, sing and dance till

p
fe - steg - giar! Cor - riam
break of day. Let's make
p
fe - steg - giar! Cor - riam
break of day. Let's make
p
fe - steg - giar! Cor - riam tut - ti,
break of day. Let's make mer - ry,
p
fe - steg - giar! Cor - riam tut - ti,
break of day. Let's make mer - ry,
p
fe - steg - giar! Cor - riam tut - ti,
break of day. Let's make mer - ry,
p
cresc.
f
tut - ti, cor - riam tut - ti, cor - riam tut - ti, cor - riam
mer - ry, let's make mer - ry, and to joy - ous strains of
cresc.
f
tut - ti, cor - riam tut - ti, cor - riam tut - ti, cor - riam
mer - ry, let's make mer - ry, and to joy - ous strains of
cresc.
f
cor - riam tut - ti, cor - riam tut - ti, cor - riam
let's make mer - ry, and to joy - ous strains of
cresc.
f
cor - riam tut - ti, cor - riam tut - ti, cor - riam
let's make mer - ry, and to joy - ous strains of
cresc.
f
cor - riam tut - ti, cor - riam tut - ti, cor - riam
let's make mer - ry, and to joy - ous strains of
cresc.
f

tut - ti, cor - riam tut - ti a fe - steg - giar, a
mu - sic, sing and dance till break of day, till
tut - ti, cor - riam tut - ti a fe - steg - giar, a
mu - sic, sing and dance till break of day, till
tut - ti, cor - riam tut - ti a fe - steg - giar, a
mu - sic, sing and dance till break of day, till
tut - ti, cor - riam tut - ti a fe - steg - giar, a
mu - sic, sing and dance till break of day, till
tut - ti, cor - riam tut - ti a fe - steg - giar, a
mu - sic, sing and dance till break of day, till
fe - steg - giar, a fe - steg - giar, a
break of day, till break of day, till
fe - steg - giar, a fe - steg - giar, a
break of day, till break of day, till
fe - steg - giar, a fe - steg - giar, a
break of day, till break of day, till
fe - steg - giar, a fe - steg - giar, a
break of day, till break of day, till
fe - steg - giar, a fe - steg - giar, a
break of day, till break of day, till
3
3
3
3
3
3
3
3

End of the Opera